CABINETS OF CURIOSITIES

COLLECTIONS OF THE VANCOUVER MUSEUM 1894-1981

Director
Robert D. Watt

Archaeology Department

Decorative and Applied Arts Department
Carol E. Mayer, *Curator*

Ethnology Department
Lynn Maranda, *Curator*

History Department
Ivan Sayers, *Curator*

Natural History Department

Published with the assistance of:
The National Museums of Canada;
The Government of British Columbia;
Ministry of the Provincial Secretary, Cultural Services Branch
Vancouver Museum Trustees Special Projects Fund.

Published by Vancouver Museums and Planetarium Association, 1100 Chestnut Street, Vancouver, British Columbia.

ISBN 0-919253-06-7
Design by: Samuel Graphic Arts Ltd.

Typesetting by: Trio Type

Colour Separation, printing and binding in Canada by Mitchell Press Ltd.

Front cover: G.M. Studios
Photography: Henry Tabbers

Stone sculpture, *India*
Donor:
Mr. G. Anderson, 1911
Cat. No. DE 207

THE VANCOUVER MUSEUM

1100 CHESTNUT STREET, VANCOUVER, B.C. V6J 3J9 • (604) 736-4431 • OPERATED BY THE VANCOUVER MUSEUMS AND PLANETARIUM ASSOCIATION

F O R E W O R D

The permanent collections of the Vancouver Museum are now the largest administered and interpreted by any civic museum in Canada. Their diversity and quality attract the interest of scholars and lay visitors alike. For various good reasons, including limited space and conservation requirements for the material, the entire collection is never constantly on view. However, one of our most important current objectives is to make as much of the collection and as wide a variety of material accessible as is practical.

Cabinets of Curiositites is one response to this aim. It is also a salute to the thousands of donors whose public spiritedness has enriched the cultural life of Vancouver for nearly a century. Since the history of the city has influenced these gifts, the exhibition also celebrates the multi-cultural character of our heritage; a Canadian community deeply influenced by Europe and Asia.

The staff are proud to present this selected guide to a unique collection.

Robert D. Watt
Director

C O N T E N T S

PREFACE

In the exhibition Cabinets of Curiosities each gallery was organized chronologically, beginning with the first donation of a 'stuffed' white swan and ending with one of the most recent donations, a Japanese bridal kimono. The development of the museum was illustrated by those objects that once belonged to people who travelled from many parts of the world to settle in Vancouver and become part of its history.

Having no delineated departments or collections policy the museum had no real guidelines and the collections grew somewhat randomly, very much parallelling the development experienced by most museums. The result was both fascinating and eclectic, but so wide in scope that it was utlimately necessary to create five curatorial departments to care for the ever-growing collections.

In this catalogue objects from the five departments of Archaeology, Decorative and Applied Arts, Ethnology, History and Natural History are presented within the geographic framework of North and South America, Asia, Europe, Oceania and Africa. This order of presentation will enable the reader to gain a clear picture of the extent of the museum's holdings. Also, whereas in the exhibition the objects were used mainly as documentary evidence, in this catalogue the selected objects are highlighted as being characteristic of specific aspects of the collection.

This publication has been prepared by the three curators on permanent staff: Lynn Maranda, Carol Mayer and Ivan Sayers who gratefully acknowledge the assistance of the following: The National Museums of Canada, GM Studios, Aphrodite Bough, Beth Carter, David Larson, Jayne Leslie, Peggy Martin, Merry Meradith, Eilish McKendy, John McLeod, Joan Meyers, Nancy Schmid and Anna Sumpton.

Carol Mayer
Exhibition and Catalogue coordinator.

The Carnegie Library.

CABINETS OF CURIOSITIES

A History of the Vancouver Museum

In March 1912, an editorial writer in The Vancouver World drew attention to the imminent opening of the Museum of the City of London and suggested that Vancouver should develop "a museum which will grow with the city and help the city grow". The Vancouver Museum's growth has been shaped by the city it serves; by Vancouver's size, economy, geographic position, people and history. However, it owes both its beginning and many of its successes to individual efforts and the vision showed by a dedicated few.

Some of the museum's essential characteristics were apparent from the start. Of these, the most important was the dual objective of preserving the city's past and providing the people of the city with an opportunity to appreciate the natural world and the works of man from other cultures and other lands. Not surprisingly, an interest in preserving the relics of civic and provincial history was not a pressing matter for most of the immigrants who swelled Vancouver's population during the first decade of its growth. But there was a small group interested in the arts, natural history and especially in the unique cultures and splendid artforms of the native peoples of the region. In the early 1890's, concern was being expressed about the disappearance of these cultures and the movement of the material objects created by the coastal Indians out of the province. Preserving this heritage was one of the main objectives of the Art, Historical and Scientific Association,

The Museum's first exhibition.

founded in the spring of 1894. Shortly after its organizational meeting, the association opened Vancouver's first museum exhibition in rented premises on the top floor of the Dunn Building on Granville Street.

A photograph still exists showing the advertising banner strung across the building asking visitors to view an exhibition of "paintings and curios". Among these curios were Northwest Coast Indian artifacts which had been purchased by several members of the Association in the previous year. In the decades that followed, the Association demonstrated again and again, its concern for local native cultures via programmes of purchase, publishing and exhibition.

But these activities lay a little in the future. Within months of the exhibition in the Dunn Building, objects were being donated to the museum's collections. The first donations tended to be natural history specimens, ethnographic artifacts and art objects. They set an eclectic and multi-disciplinary pattern that reflected the interests of the Association members and their supporters and the cosmopolitan nature of Vancouver's population. Even though resources were very limited, the Association was not wholly a passive receptacle for whichever objects were offered. Regular purchasing began in 1898 and had actually been undertaken prior to the Association's establishment. The first purchases were mainly Coast Indian artifacts but on one occasion, a significant sum was spent acquiring some Japanese sword guards.

This activity on collections development gave added impetus to the question of a building. In turn, this raised the question of involvement with the City Council and the possible status of the museum as a public institution. On 16th June, 1898, City Council gave the Association a grant of $100 towards the museum operation. At virtually the same time, the Association opened negotiations with the City on the question of space for the museum in the new library building, then being planned for a site at the corner of Main and Hastings. As a result of these discussions, the Association was incorporated on May 8th, 1901 and two years later on 26th August, 1903 reached agreement with the City. Title to the museum collection passed to the City in return for provision of "convenient and suitable premises. . . where the collection may be exhibited and stored". It was agreed at the same time that the museum would be housed on the top floor of the new Carnegie Library. The City Museum formally opened in this new location on April 19th, 1905. For the next half century, the museum's physical die was cast, as was its relationship with the City. With the Association as governors, and the City as owner of the collections and principal funder, the museum struggled to grow with Vancouver and help it grow. Despite physical and fiscal restraints which grew increasingly desperate by mid century, the museum achieved some notable successes with a paid staff of one and a very active body of volunteers.

During this half century the Association through the City Museum spearheaded two projects of special note which reflected long-standing Association and museum interests. Between 1915 and 1925, the Association attempted to establish, in Stanley Park, a reconstructed Coast Indian village built around some major totem and house poles and ceremonial objects acquired in the early 1920's. These plans proved too ambitious but the poles were set up in the park, anticipating by almost three decades plans in Victoria and Vancouver to provide open-air interpretation of the splendid Coast Indian cultures.

As the years passed, more attention was also paid to the matter of the archaeological heritage of the region. One of the most important prehistoric sites on the whole coast was within civic boundaries; the great midden at Marpole, on the north bank of the Fraser. One of the most faithful and most active

Museum Gallery in Carnegie Library building.

Association supporters in its first half-century, anthropologist Charles Hill-Tout, made some very preliminary investigations of the midden in 1902. Then in 1930 the Museum sponsored a more extensive series of investigations and the artifacts located in that year became the premier portion of an expanding local archaeology collection.

By the end of the Second World War, the museum's housing crisis had become acute and yet substantial change in the situation was still twenty years away. What unfolded as a transitional and pivotal decade began in 1957 with the move of the public library to new quarters on Burrard Street. The space vacated was turned over to the Museum which effectively tripled the available display and storage area. There was no increase in staff however, and neither the building nor staffing levels conformed to any contemporary thinking about the nature of a modern museum. Two years later, there was a dramatic shift in the relationship between the Association and the city, some of the impetus coming from the opening of the Maritime Museum in 1958. The two museums became a city department under the control of a Civic Museum Board with the Association having representation on the Board and becoming a kind of

The Vancouver Museums and Planetarium Complex.

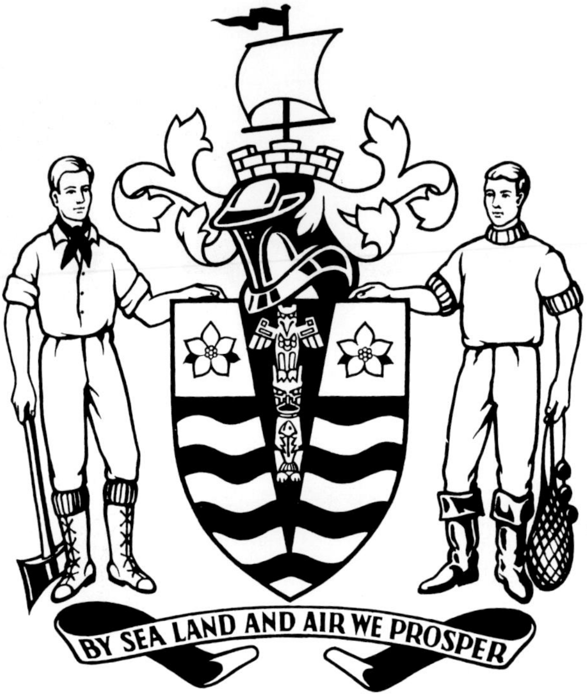

The coat of arms of the City of Vancouver.

"Friends of the Museum" auxiliary and the city's official museum membership organization. It was hoped that this new board could develop an overall policy for the city's museum and propose a solution to the need for a new home. The Heinrich Report of 1965 recommended building a new museum on the south shore of False Creek near the Burrard Bridge. Federal and provincial monies made available for the 1967 Confederation Centennial projects meant that 74 years after its establishment the city museum, now re-named the Centennial Museum, moved into a new building, the first designed and built for it.

The history of the museum as a contemporary institution, staffed by a sizeable number of trained professionals, with exhibits reflecting current thinking in the museum world about design and interpretation dates from October 1968, when the new building was opened at Vanier Park. Until that time, the collections had been developed and administered as a single unit; now divisions of natural history, archaeology, ethnology and history appeared. An ambitious programme of permanent exhibitions and fieldwork was launched. In 1972, the city relinquished its direct management in favour of the old pattern. The Museums and Planetarium Association, the lineal descendant of the old Art, Historical and Scientific Association became the governing authority, with the largest single source of funding being an annual civic grant. In 1977, the museum's basic objectives were clarified and updated. This new statement contained some elements of the 1894 objectives but shifted the museum's role in terms of heritage preservation to match changes in Vancouver itself and recognized that the museum was now a partner in regional cultural services and not "the only game in town". This new statement defined the museum as an institution for

> "collecting, documenting, preserving, exhibiting and interpreting the human and natural history of the Lower Mainland region of British Columbia with special emphasis given to the development of collections and exhibitions of the decorative and applied arts from the three cultures forming the principal heritage of the region: Canada, Europe and Asia".

The return of the Association as direct manager coincided with the promulgation of the new federal policy of democratization and decentralization of museums. One of the first concrete results of that policy was the establishment of the national network of Associate Museums. The museum was given associate status in 1974 and with it, began to receive operating assistance from Ottawa for the first time. Later in the decade, the federal government passed the Cultural Property Export and Import Act and in September 1977, the museum was designated as a category A institution within the framework of that important legislation. Help was also forthcoming from the provincial government. A new programme of operating assistance was established in 1981 which resulted, for the first time, in significant operating support being received from all three levels of government.

In 1979, a new curatorial department was founded, Decorative and Applied Arts, to give structural expression to the important policy changes. During the first two years of its existence the new department was the focal point for the development of the museum's most ambitious project, The Look of Music exhibition. In less than a hundred years, the museum, with the creation of this exhibition, had proved that it could serve the city and expand cultural horizons in a very professional and highly dramatic way. The support given by many groups and individuals in the community was another important and significant feature of this project. As the museum prepares to play a major role in the city's centennial in 1986 and plans for its own in 1994, the future seems bright.

Robert D. Watt
Director

Stained Glass and etched window by William Morris and Company, designed by Edward Burne-Jones. Museum Purchase: 1979.

THE AMERICAS

Passenger Pigeon.
Ectopistes Migratorius

The Passenger Pigeon was one of the most abundant of all bird species. Unfortunately, the last known specimen died in the Cincinnati Zoological Gardens in 1914. The birds inhabited most forested areas of eastern North America and were found occasionally on the Pacific coast and in Europe.

Donor:
Mr. Leo Malfet, c. 1935

Trumpeter Swan.
Olor Buccinator

One of North America's largest birds, the Trumpeter Swan can weigh up to 12.5 kg. It nests in the dense vegetation of marshes, lakes and rivers, and ranges from southern Alaska into British Columbia, Alberta and the north-western United States. Once an endangered species, the Trumpeter Swan is now protected by law.

The specimen illustrated is the first recorded donation given to the museum.

Donor:
Mr. Sidney Williams, 1895

Northwestern Crow.
Corvus Caurinus

The Northwestern Crow is approximately 41-43 cm long and is a close relative of the Common Crow. Its usual habitat is either shoreline or tidewater areas near the edges of coastal forests. It ranges from southern Alaska to north-western Washington State. The albino crow on the left illustrates a congenital deficiency of colour pigment, producing the distinctive white plumage.

Donors:
(left) Stanley Park Commissioner, c. 1913
(right) Anonymous, c. 1965

Striped Skunk.
Mephitis Mephitis (Albino)

Adult Striped Skunks may measure up to 70 cm. including the long bushy tail. The animal is noted for emitting a distinctive offensive odour when attacked or killed. Natural habitats are open fields, marshes and streamside thickets. As with the albino crow also illustrated on this page, this skunk exhibits the traits of albinism.

Donor:
Miss P. Kirstiuk, 1980

Great Blue Heron.
Ardea herodias

Great Blue Herons are found in the northern parts of South America, and in all but the coldest wetlands of North America. They grow to a maximum height of 120 cm. and are often mistaken for cranes. Cranes, however, are generally more wary and they project their heads forward, in flight, whereas the Great Blue Heron flies with the neck folded back on the shoulder.

Donor:
Vancouver Natural History Society, 1975

Mammal Skulls.
British Columbia

The museum has a collection of over fifty mammal skulls used for display and study purposes. The largest donation came from Mr. T.V. Mould, a trapper in Fort Nelson, B.C.
The largest skull illustrated is that of a Black Bear (*Ursus Americanus*). To its left is a Coyote (*Canis latrans*) and to its right, a Bobcat (*Lynx rufous*).

Donors: (Black Bear)
Mr. Walter M. Draycott, 1939
(Coyote and Bobcat)
Mr. T.V. Mould, 1947

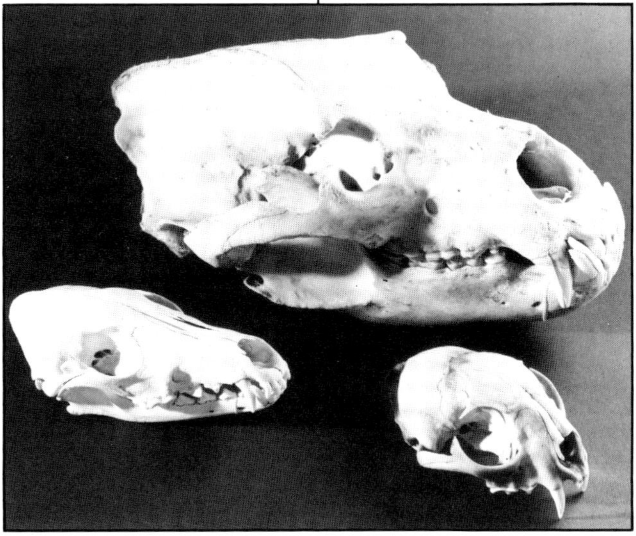

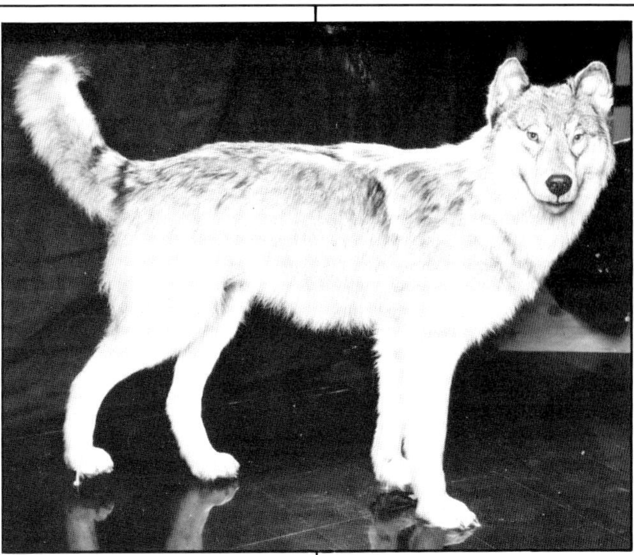

Grey Wolf.
Canis Lupus

Wolves are the largest of the dog-like carnivores, sometimes reaching a weight of 63.5 k. Habitats are open plains, forests, mountains and bushlands. In British Columbia, wolves are found everywhere from the rainforests of the coastal islands to coniferous and deciduous woodlands of the mainland, extending to the high plateaux of the provincial interior.

Museum purchase, 1971

Bowl. *Queen Charlotte Islands, British Columbia, date unknown*

The famous stone carvings of the Pacific North-West have been the source of much speculation. They are usually presumed to have had some ceremonial or ritualistic function. The museum has an interesting and well-known collection, a few of which are shown on these two pages. This bowl has a face carved at each end, but it is difficult to ascertain whether the features are intended to be human or animal. The bowl becomes even more intriguing when one notices that the eyes of one face seem to have vision and the eyes of the other face are apparently sightless. As with many of the stone carvings of the Pacific North-West, this bowl poses a number of questions yet to be answered. Length 27 cm.

Donor:
Mr. J.I. Sweet, 1978
Cat. No. QAA 2241

Stone Carvings.
British Columbia, dates unknown

Many of the carvings found in British Columbia portray non-human figures and are generally referred to as zoomorphic. The bowl at the top of the picture was found in Quatsino Sound; the club in the middle, believed to represent a kingfisher, and the bird-shaped bowl were found in the Fraser Valley. These carvings may have had some ceremonial or ritualistic function. Lengths (top) 27 cm., (middle) 45 cm., (bottom) 23 cm.

Donors: Anonymous
Cat. Nos. QAA 1085 (top), QAA 1070 (middle), QAA 1082 (bottom)

Stone Carvings.
British Columbia, dates unknown

The club on the left is referred to as a 'slave killer' and is believed to have been used by the Northern groups, in this case the Kwakiutl, for the ritual killing of slaves. The uses for the two human figure bowls, both found in the Fraser Valley, are unclear. Some anthropologists have associated them with female puberty rites while others have suggested that they were used by shamans in connection with their curing or divining functions. Although there may continue to be controversy over the uses of these stone carvings, there is little doubt that they date from the earliest age of Coast Indian art. (left to right) length 36.7 cm., height 21.7 cm., length 16 cm.

Donors:
(left and middle) Anonymous
(right) Miss. E. Bonsall, 1956
Cat. Nos. (left to right) QAA 1067, QAA 1076, QAA 1086

Bowl.
Pacific Northwest Coast — Kwakiutl, date unknown.

This unpainted bowl is carved in the form of a seal from a single piece of cedar wood. Bowls such as this and the one pictured below, were, for their owners, symbols of wealth and prestige and were used for holding food at feasts (a large communal meal) or at potlatches (an elaborate meal and occasion on which gifts were exchanged). Large spoons or ladles were used to transfer the food to smaller bowls for distribution to individual serving dishes. Length: 86 cm.

Donor: Mr. Claude L. Harrison, 1958
Cat. No. AA 722

Bowl.
Pacific Northwest Coast — Kwakiutl, c. 1900

This bowl consists of three interlocking parts, each carved from a single piece of red cedar wood. It is carved in the form of *Sisiutl* (double-headed serpent) and has coloured areas of black, red, white and green paint. Circa 1900, the Chief of the Kwickwasiutaneuk people, John Scow (Muhlas, c. 1870-1934), who had inherited the rights and privileges to the use of *Sisiutl,* commissioned Kakuglasima Wadagha to carve this bowl. In the early 1900's the bowl was used in ceremonials at Gwayasdums and Gwayee, not only by Chief John Scow, but also by his two brothers, Peter and George Scow, both chiefs of the Tsawadeneuk people. Total length: 3.96 m.

Purchased for the City of Vancouver by H.R. McMillan, 1964.
Cat. No. AA 2268 a, b, c.

Chest.
Pacific Northwest Coast — Haida, 19th Century

Carved from argillite, the chest consists of a removable lid bearing sculptured bird, serpent, frog and human head figures, and a box on which there are sculptured figures of a lion (sides —head and forepaws on front; rump, tail and hind paws on back) and two wolf heads (one at each end). Carving of the chest is attributed to Charles Edenshaw (Tahaygen, c. 1839-1924), reputedly the most famous and productive of all Haida artists. Although originally reported to have been purchased c. 1882 by Dr. Israel Powell, the first Indian Commissioner for B.C., the chest has also been known as the "Spencer" box. However, no reason for this attribution can be found. Total length: 50.8 cm.

Donor: Mrs. Jonathan Rogers, 1944
Cat. No. AA 61

Sculpture.
Pacific Northwest Coast — Haida, date unknown

This sculptured canoe filled with nine figures, eight human and one in the form of a bear, is carved from argillite and decorated with ivory inlay. The human figures represented are: three whale hunters holding harpoons and wearing what appear to be southwesters; a Chief, flanked by two smaller figures which are visible on the reverse side; a canoeman, also on the reverse side; and a female figure facing the bear. Carving of the piece is attributed to Charles Edenshaw (Tahaygen, c. 1839-1924). In addition to being a premier craftsman, Edenshaw was also a Chief. As a young man he went to live with his maternal uncle, Albert Edward Edenshaw of Kiusta, Chief of the Stastas Eagle Clan, whom he succeeded in 1894. Length: 31.75 cm.

Museum purchase: 1927
Cat. No. AA 60

Plate.
Pacific Northwest Coast — Haida, c. 1900.

Like the two preceding pieces, this shallow plate is carved of argillite and attributed to Charles Edenshaw (Tahaygen, c. 1839-1924). The design on the plate illustrates the theme of the underwater wealth spirit known as *Wasco* (Sea Wolf) or *Gonakadet*. Here, the body of Wasco curves around the circular field. A human figure (possibly a spirit) is held in its mouth, and two whales appear, one beside the ear and the other within the tail. Although Edenshaw did not sign his work, his style is recognized by the superb quality of the engraving and the distinctive shapes of his formlines and other design elements. While he also produced work in wood, silver, and ivory, his principal medium was argillite, a type of slate. Mineralogically, argillite is composed largely of the clay mineral kaolinite, a hydrated aluminum silicate, and is an unusual rock in that it contains virtually no quartz or feldspar. It is therefore particularly well suited for carving. The blackness is due to organic debris. A single rockslide quarry on the side of Slatechuck Mountain near Skidegate is the source of the argillite used by the Haida for carvings. Fostered by the curio trade with white explorers, carving in argillite is generally believed to have started about 1820 and always has been a commercial art. Diameter: 38.1 cm.

Museum Purchase: 1959
Cat. No. AA 49

Basket.
Northern Interior — Chilcotin, c. 1890-1900

Woven from spruce root, this coiled basket is completely imbricated with grass and cherry back, the latter comprising the naturalistic designs depicting horse and bird figures. A withe encircles the outside of the basket near the top and is held in place, originally by spruce root but now mainly by wire. Thongs looped around the withe were used to hold the tump-line by which the basket was carried. This example is typical of the Chilcotin burden baskets which were used to carry food and personal belongings. Length: 45.7 cm. Width: 35.6 cm.

Donation/Transfer: Edward and Mary Lipsett, 1941/1971
Cat. No. AC 215

Box.
Pacific Northwest Coast, date unknown

The sides of the box consist of one piece of red cedar wood which has been kerfed transversely at three carefully measured points, steamed at these kerfs, and bent. Small holes have been drilled diagonally through the joining corner and the joint secured with hardwood pegs. The bottom is fitted and joined (pegged) separately. An abstract design in red and black is painted on the front and repeated on the back; a single star-shaped figure in black appears on the sides. Boxes such as this one were used to store valuables and, occasionally, in trade with other groups. Height: 17.8cm.

Donor:
Miss Keith Estate, 1958
Cat. No. AA 900

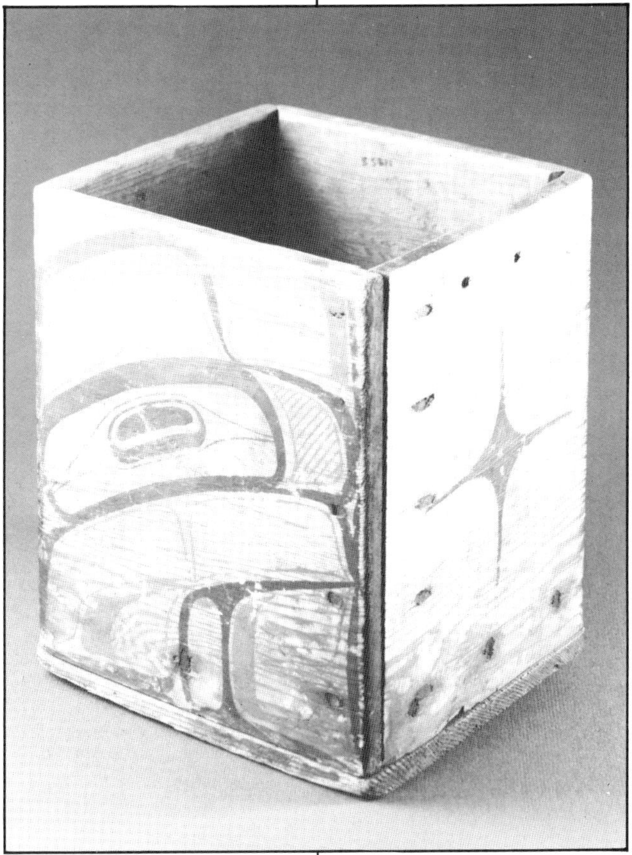

Cradle.
Pacific Northwest Coast — Kwakiutl, circa 1900.

Made from red cedar wood, the two sides and foot comprise one piece which has been kerfed, steamed and bent. The headboard and bottom have been added separately. On the inside of the headboard, the carved and painted design depicts either the sun or moon, and around the outside, painted designs of two sea otters, killer whale, bear, and salmon-trout head appear. The cradle contains a latticed wooden platform covered with shredded cedar bark and moss. It is believed that this cradle had a ceremonial function. Length: 55.9 cm.

Donor:
Mrs. J. Buntzen, 1903
Cat. No. AA 923

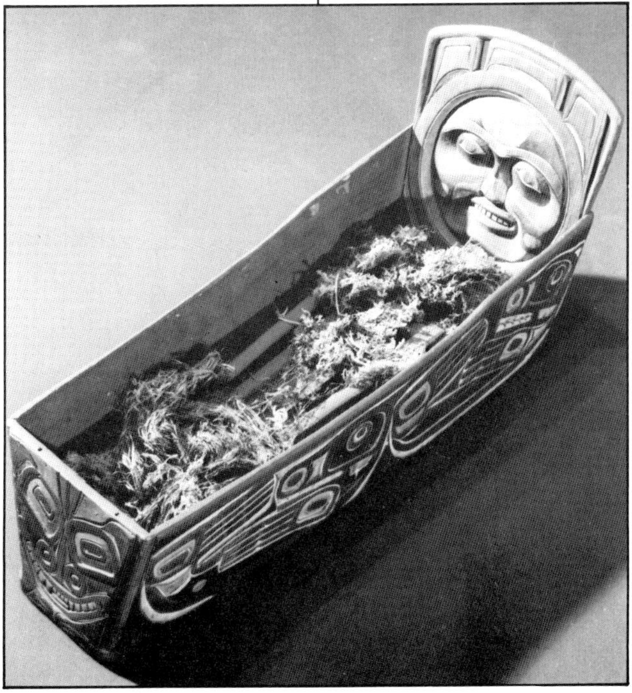

Sculptures.
Pacific Northwest Coast — Nahwitti Kwakiutl, 19th Century

These unpainted sculptured figures are carved in human form from alder wood. Two of the figures are masked; one holds a staff and another wears a headdress. Their small size suggests that they may have been part of a shaman's regalia. Collected prior to 1900 from Nigei Island by the donor and his father, Reverend Ebenezer Robson, they were brought to the Museum c. 1936. Three sets of replicas were made, one set being kept by the Museum and the others sent to the Winnipeg and the British Museums. Heights: 14 cm.

Donor:
E.S. Robson, 1948
Cat. Nos. (left to right)
AA 679, AA 676, AA 677, AA 678

"Boneshaker" Bicycle.
Barkerville, B.C., c. 1864

Made by an unknown craftsman in the Gold Rush town of Barkerville, this iron bicycle is reputed to be the oldest surviving wheeled vehicle manufactured in British Columbia. The wooden wheels are rimmed with iron, and the power is direct drive with the pedals mounted on the front axle. Its great weight combined with a total lack of braking mechanism made the bicycle difficult to control, and the cyclist would have been violently shaken as he rode on unpaved streets.
Length 2.4 m.

Donor:
Mr. John Stuison, 1909
Cat. No. H971.393.1

Alderman's Desk.
Vancouver, November 1886

The City of Vancouver was incorporated on April 6, 1886, and by November of that year the new City Hall on Powell Street was ready for occupation. Mayor M.A. McLean presided over ten council members, each using a wooden desk as shown in the photograph.
Height 91.5 cm.

Donor:
Vancouver City Archives, 1972
Cat. No. H972.3.114

Man's Bathing Suit.
Vancouver, 1921-1938

Beginning in 1912, bathing suits could be rented from the Vancouver Parks Board through the various bath houses dotted along the city beaches. The original models were even more modest than the style shown here, which was first available in 1921.

The suits were made of knitted black wool, decorated with coloured bands around the rib cage and the name of the appropriate bath house embroidered on the chest. A large "C.V." (City of Vancouver) and an inventory number were stencilled on the back. Length 64 cm.

Museum Purchase, 1979
Cat. No. H979.49.1

Police Badges.
Vancouver, 1890-1950

The oldest badge in this collection is the helmet plate, second from the left in the lower row. This form was based on British helmet plates with the officer's number clearly visible at centre. This badge style was discontinued c. 1928.

The three star badges on the right of the photograph were worn on the chest from c. 1900 to c. 1935. These emblems were hand-cut, engraved sterling silver.

The remaining star and shield are later, mass-produced badges made of steel. Average width 7 cm.

Donor:
Vancouver Police Department, 1974
Cat. No. H974.33.34-40

Home Canning Machine.
Vancouver, 1917

In 1809 Francois Appert, a Parisian confectioner, succeeded in preserving food in specially made glass jars. His experiments had been prompted by an offer of 12,000 francs posted by the French government in 1795 for the invention of a method of preserving food for the military forces. A

steel "tin" cannister was introduced in the 1830's and the modern, double-seamed tin without hand-soldering was available by 1908.

The machine illustrated is the prototype of the domestic tin-canner invented by the Vancouver pioneer, Mr. F.W. Burpee. Mr. Burpee came to Vancouver c. 1890 and in 1896 was co-founder of Letson and Burpee, Machinists and Founders. This invention was one of more than thirty patented by Mr. Burpee and was designed to provide an inexpensive, convenient method of home canning in tins rather than jars.

The machine was very successful and the company claimed sales of 150,000 by 1940. Height 33.6 cm.

Donor:
Vancouver City Archives, 1973
Cat. No. H973.823.1

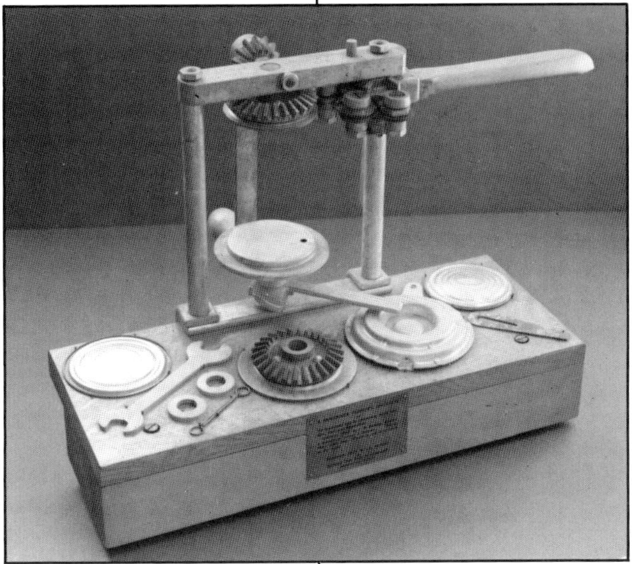

Toiletries.
Vancouver, 1930-1950

These articles are a small selection of the goods stocked by Lam Wah Bong at the Herbalist Drug Store, which he operated from 1916 to 1975 in Shanghai Alley and at 122 East Pender Street. Mr. Lam stored any merchandise which did not sell, and when he retired much of his back inventory was purchased by the Vancouver Museum. Although these objects are not truly antique, they are pristine examples of the cosmetics, toiletries and packaging styles of the 1930's, 1940's and 1950's. In addition, the museum holds a large number of posters and other promotional advertising used in the store, as well as an extensive collection of school supplies dating back to the 1920's.

Museum Purchase, 1976
Cat. No. H976.65.1

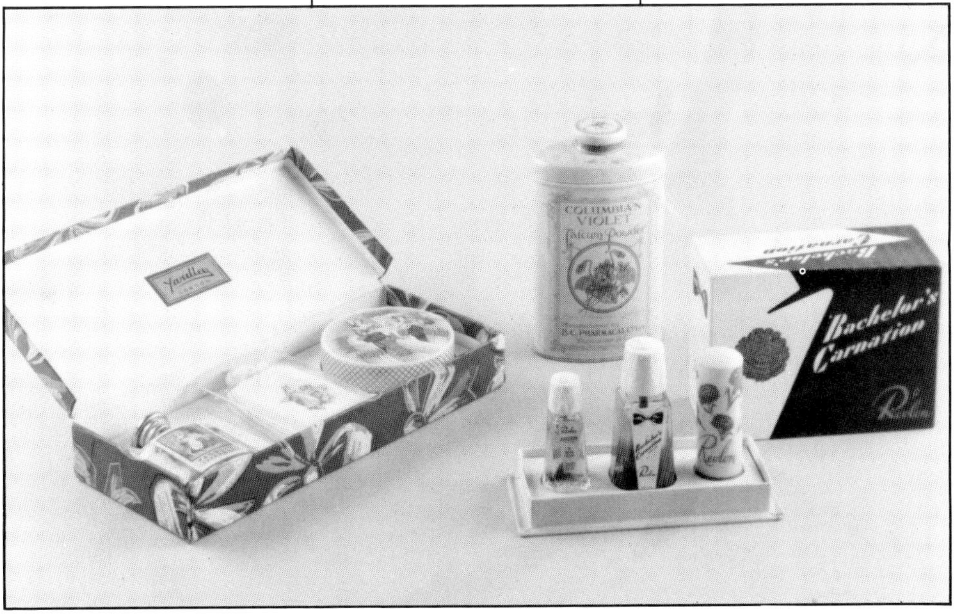

Autophone Gramophone.
Vancouver, c. 1913

A true rarity in the world of gramophones, this machine was designed to play twelve cylinder records automatically in sequence. On the average, a record would play for slightly over four minutes, enabling the machine to reproduce music unattended for almost one hour. The manufacturer hoped that restaurants would purchase the Autophone to provide musical entertainment for their customers.

The machine is also remarkable for having been built in Vancouver.
Height 118 cm.

Donor:
Vancouver City Archives, 1972
Cat. No. H975.141.1

Street Photographer's Camera.
Vancouver, 1946-1979

Foncie Pulice and his street camera were as much a part of the Vancouver scene as the Birks' Clock or the Hotel Vancouver. In 1934, Foncie first worked as a street photographer for Mr. Joe Iaci. After being demobbed in 1947 he began working independently, using this camera made from war surplus material. He snapped literally millions of photographs during his career in Vancouver's main streets and parks and there are few homes in the city without at least one "Foncie's Foto" tucked safely away.

Mr. Pulice's contribution to the city is greater than his modesty admits and the best testimonial to his success is the affection his patrons still feel for the snapshots of them which he took over his many working years.
Height 132 cm.

Donor:
Mr. A. Pulice, 1979
Cat. No. H980.6.1

The Barclay Chair.
c. 1775

This chair, made in the Malacca Straits in the third quarter of the 18th Century, belonged to Captain Charles William Barclay, commander of the British ship, *Imperial Eagle*. In 1787 Captain Barclay was responsible for the discovery of the Strait of Juan de Fuca, the body of water separating southern Vancouver Island from the north-western corner of what is now Washington State. The Strait was further explored in 1792 by Captain George Vancouver, who discovered the site of the future harbour of Vancouver, British Columbia.

This beautiful chair, which was used on board the *Imperial Eagle* in 1787, is valuable to the museum not only for its association with one of our earliest explorers, but also as a fine example of 18th Century Oriental export furniture. Captain Barclay's great-great-grandson, Major V.A.H. Denne, presented the chair to the Vancouver City Archives who, in turn, transferred ownership to the Vancouver Museum.
Height 89 cm.

Donor:
Vancouver City Archives, 1976
Cat. No. H976.35.50

Judicial Chair.
British Columbia, c. 1860's

In 1858 the mainland colony of British Columbia was established by an Act of the British Parliament. In that same year, Sir Matthew Baillie Begbie arrived from England to become the first Chief Justice of the colony, and he was quick to establish his legal authority. In fact the orderliness and lack of crime during the Gold Rush in the British Columbia interior were most probably the result of Begbie's rigid, but fair, enforcement of the law.

His sense of theatre and his respect for the Crown are well shown in this, his judicial chair. Simple, almost stark in design, it is over 1.6 m. tall and was intended to impress the courtroom with its exaggerated size.

Donor:
Vancouver City Archives, 1972
Cat. No. H977.516.1

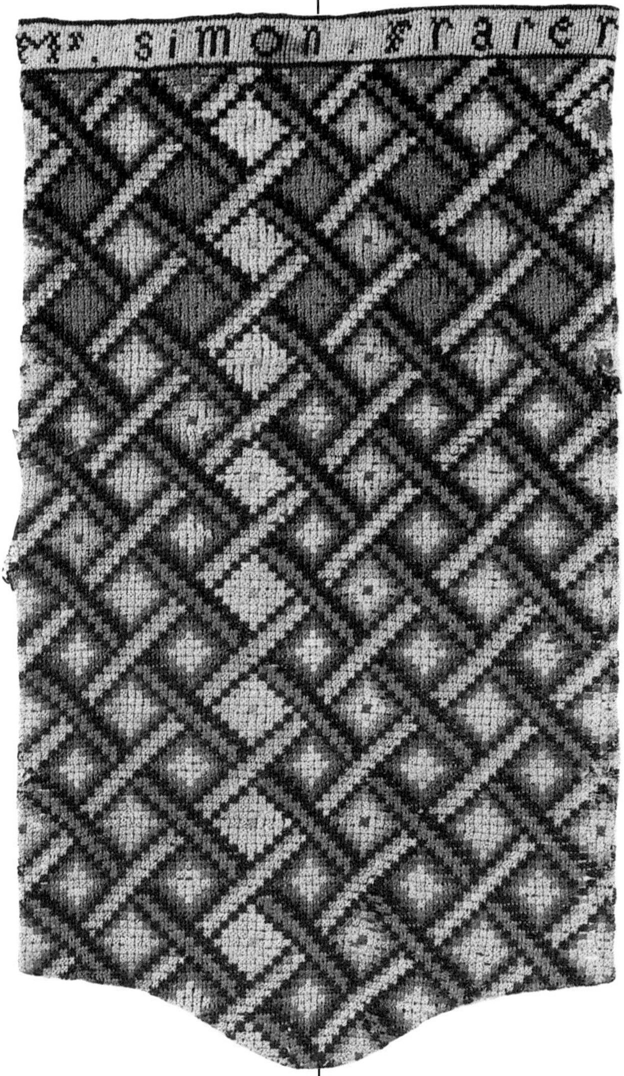

Embroidered Panel.
Upper Canada, post 1820

Simon Fraser (1776-1862) was a prominent figure in the history of British Columbia. He founded Fort McLeod, the first trading post west of the Rockies, and in 1808 commanded the third expedition to cross overland from the prairies to the Pacific coast. On this journey, as a representative of the Northwest Company, he became the first European to travel the tortuous Fraser River.

The embroidered panel shown in the photograph is part of a table-top fire screen worked by his wife and is thought to represent an interpretation of the Fraser tartan. He and his wife died in poverty on the same day (April 19, 1862) after forty-two years of happy marriage. Length 39 cm.

Donor:
Simon Fraser University, 1976
Cat. No. H976.39.14

Performance Costume.
Vancouver, 1908-1913

Pauline Johnson (Tekahionwake) was born on the Six Nation Reserve, Brantford, Ontario, in 1861. Her mixed heritage and her literary education, notably in 19th Century English poets, developed in her a talent for expressing traditional Indian tales in romantic, colourful verse and prose. She felt it necessary to bridge the gap between Indian and European Canadian, and accepted almost every opportunity to take her message to the public. Miss Johnson's works were widely read but her dramatic recitations were among her most popular triumphs.

Donor:
Pauline Johnson (Estate), 1913
Cat. No. AG 27

Portrait Mask of E. Pauline Johnson.
Vancouver, 1913-1930

Charles Marega, the sculptor of the lions on the First Narrows Bridge, Vancouver, was an admirer and friend of Pauline Johnson. When she died in 1913, he cast her death mask which he used as the model for this marble portrait. He chose to show the poetess sleeping, with her delicate face half submerged in the raw stone.

The effect is almost mystical and contrasts the fragility of Pauline's features with the strength of the pure white marble. Length 34.3 cm.

Donor:
Mr. Charles Marega, c. 1930
Cat. No. H980.228.1

Powder Horn.
Canada, c. 1759

Soldier, artist and amateur poet, Sergeant Ned Botwood of the 47th Regiment of Foot has left this unique record of one of the best-known moments in Canadian history. On his powder horn he carved a map of the Battle of the Plains of Abraham fought near Quebec City on 13 September, 1759, adding a suitable memorial to his fallen leader, General James Wolfe, and the coat-of-arms of his sovereign, George III of England. In a poem wishing "confusion to the French dogs", Botwood expresses his satisfaction at the victory over the French forces of Louis XV under Montcalm. Most of those fighting on both sides were not Canadian, but the success of the British had implications which continue to affect us deeply over two hundred years later. Length 43.5 cm.

Museum Purchase: 1980
Cat. No. H980.232.1

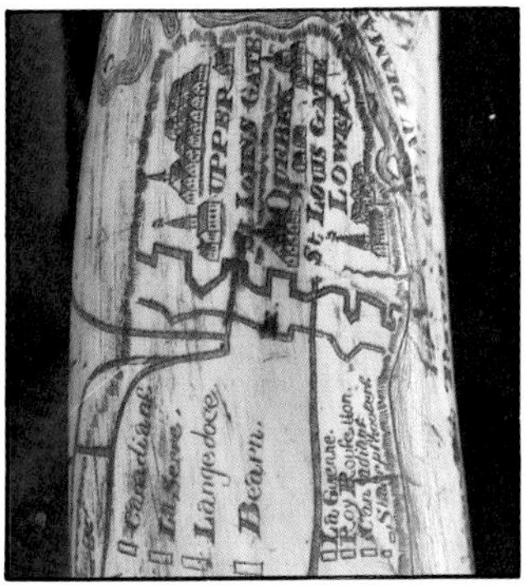

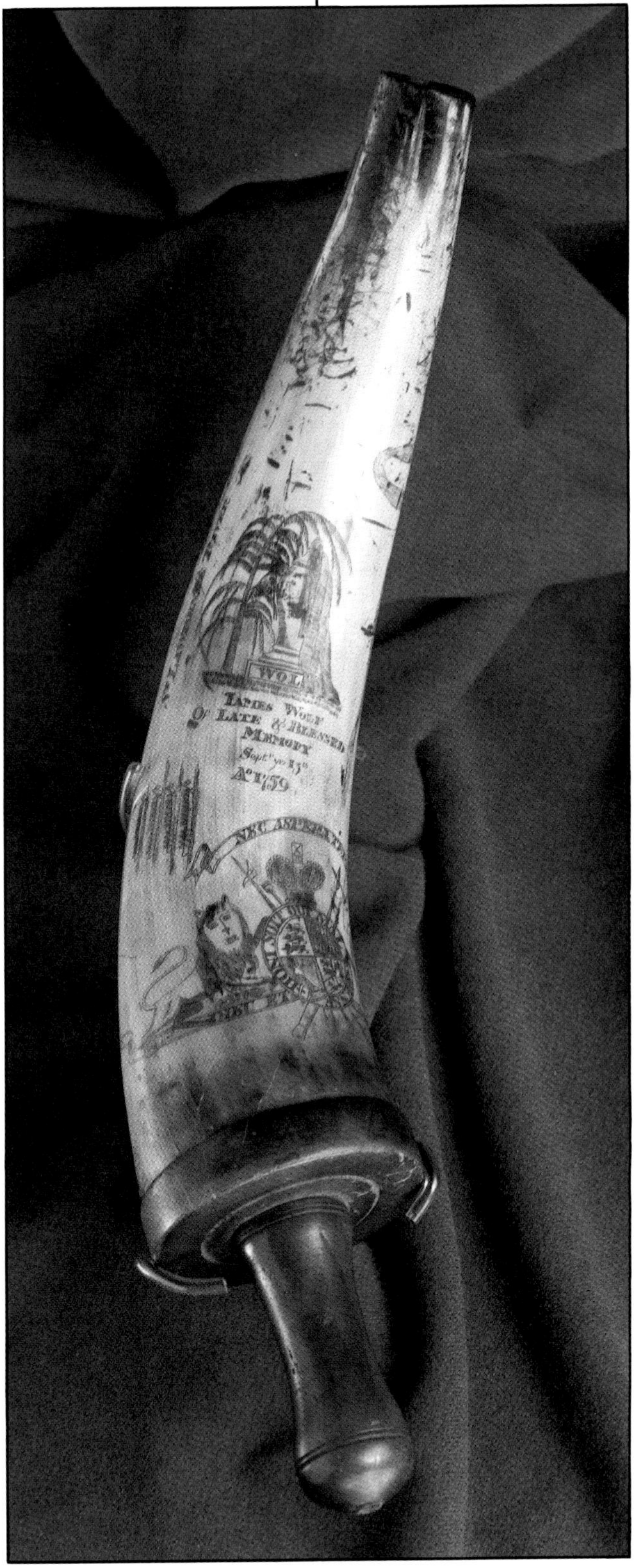

Wedding Dress.
Vancouver, 1907

This beautiful China silk dress was worn by Miss Vivian May Wharton at her wedding to Thomas Hull, an event which took place at her family home at 1142 Davie Street, June 26, 1907. Her grandfather was James Murray Yale, Hudson's Bay Company Factor at Fort Langley from 1833 to 1859.

The softly flared skirt and the puffed sleeves and bodice front are in the fashionable taste of the day. The lace yoke and collar were removable to transform the dress into a garment suitable for a formal reception or evening function. Total back length 149 cm.

Donor:
Mrs. E. Grace Collishaw, 1980
Cat. No. H980.87.4

Table Lamp.
Vancouver, c. 1908

This table lamp was constructed by Mr. Charles Bloomfield, a talented local art-glass craftsman at the turn of the century. In this piece Mr. Bloomfield was inspired by the design style of the Arts and Craft movement, and he incorporated glass panels hand-painted by a friend, Mr. Martin Malfet. These panels depict scenes of France; Blois, Limoges, Soissons and Harbor La Rochelle. Height 59 cm.

Donor:
Mrs. D. V. Sewell, 1977
Cat. No. H977.1025.1

Neon Sign.
Vancouver, 1940's

In Vancouver neon-illuminated advertising became most popular during the 1930's and 1940's and at one time this city claimed more neon footage per capita than any other city in the world.

For this reason, in 1977 The Vancouver Museum purchased over forty local neon signs from the largest collection extant.
Height 102.5 cm.

Museum Purchase: 1977
Cat. No. H977.1015.12

"Sike's" Hydrometer and Thermometer.
Barkerville Hospital, 1860's

The Sike's Hydrometer, invented in England in 1816, was used to determine the strength of liquid spirits. The large bulb is in fact a float; the number of weights required to make it submerge in a liquid, added to the measurement read from the upper stem, determines the liquid's density and, through calculation, the alcoholic proof.

This particular instrument and its accompanying thermometer were used in the hospital at Barkerville, British Columbia's most famous Gold Rush town.
Length 17.5 cm.

Donor:
Mrs. J. Horne, 1958
Cat. No. H971.231.11

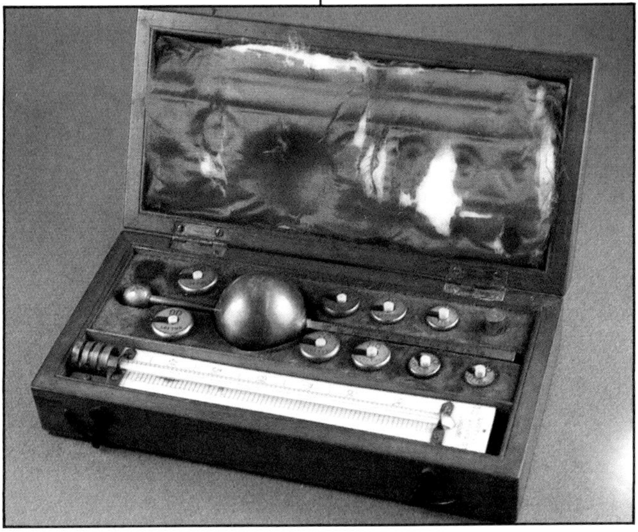

Soda Siphon Bottles.
Canada, 1886-1950

Shown here is a small selection from the Museum's collection of more than ninety soda syphon bottles, primarily the gift of one donor. These bottles are most valuable to the Museum because of their acid-etched labels, which mark their sources as long-vanished restaurants and bar rooms originally operated throughout Western Canada.

The prototype of the modern siphon bottle, the "Regency Portable Fountain", was patented in 1825 by Mr. Charles Plinth. Average height 38 cm.

Donor:
Mr. Evan Mitchell, 1981
Cat. No. H981.26.1

Frontlet.
Pacific Northwest Coast — Tsimshian, 19th Century

Dating from 1850, the frontlet depicts a squatting human figure carved from wood, partially painted, and inlaid with abalone shell. While headdress frontlets are relatively rare, this piece is also unusual in that the figure has human ears and the abalone inlay on the arms extends to the fingers. Frontlets such as this one comprise the forehead piece of headdresses worn by chiefs. Height: 19 cm.

Museum purchase: 1981
This acquisition has been made possible by a contribution from the Government of Canada under the terms of the Cultural Property Export and Import Act.
Cat. No. AA 2401

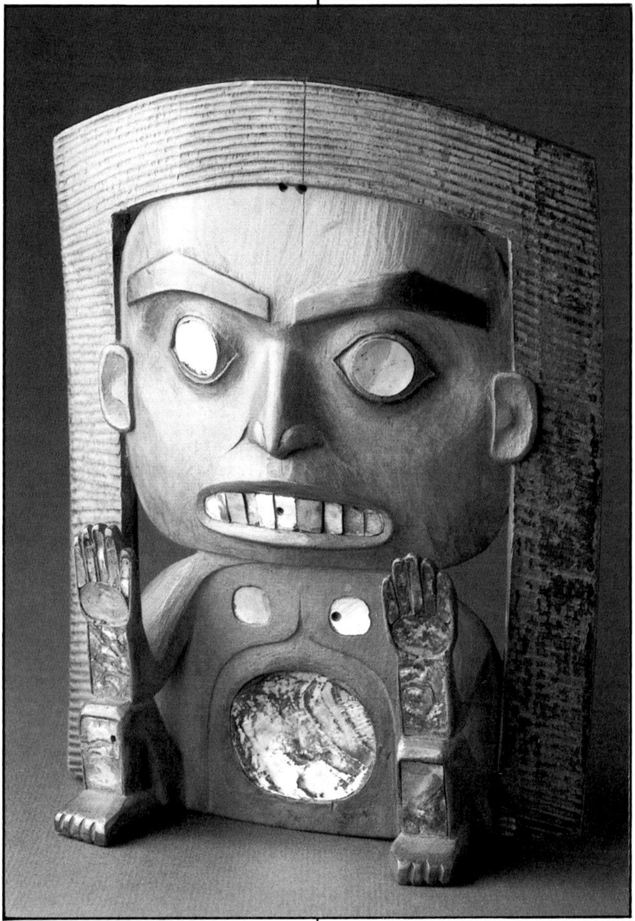

Bowl.
Pacific Northwest Coast — Haida or Tlingit, c. 1800

The bowl is carved in the form of a raven from a single piece of hardwood and partially painted in black and vermilion. Other figures represented are hawk and human and the design of the bowl is derived from that of raven rattles. It was collected in the late 19th Century by Lieutenant David Lyle of Philadelphia, the inventor of the "breeches buoy". Length: 45.7 cm.

Museum purchase: 1981
This acquisition has been made possible by a contribution from the Government of Canada under the terms of the Cultural Property Export and Import Act.
Cat. No. AA 2400

Mask.

Pacific Northwest Coast — Northern Kwakiutl, c. 1880

Carved in the form of a human face, this mask is of wood stained dark brown with faded green markings. Since it was reported to have been found in a cave in Kynock Inlet, it has been referred to as a "death mask". However, important regalia was often concealed in caves away from a village in order to avoid its seizure in the event of an enemy raid, and the resulting loss of prerogative. Its life-like human characteristics suggest its use in winter ceremonials, possibly of the *"Dluwulaxa"* series. The importance of this mask is evidenced by its exhibition record: "Yakutat South: Indian Art of the Northwest Coast" at the Art Institute of Chicago (1964); "Arts of the Raven" at the Vancouver Art Gallery (1967); "Masterpieces of Indian and Eskimo Art from Canada" at the Musée de l'Homme, Paris, France (1969) and at the National Gallery of Canada, Ottawa (1969-1970). In addition it has been widely published, most recently in "Portrait Masks from the Northwest Coast of America" by J.C.H. King, published in 1979 by Thames and Hudson, London, England. Height: 20.3 cm

Donors:
F. Nygaard and C. Cook, 1938
Cat. No. AA 123

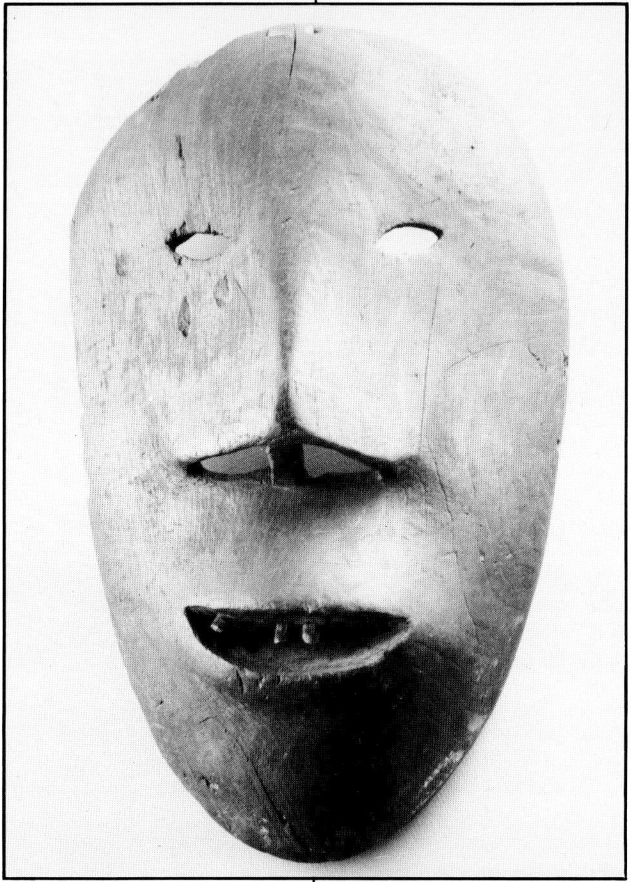

Mask.
Inuit, date unknown.

This unpainted human face mask has been carved from wood, and bone teeth have been added. Such masks were used more often for dancing than for any other activity. Most dances were of a religious nature and were directed primarily at fusing the human world to the spiritual. While dances portrayed many events of Inuit life, the greatest number were designed to ensure a continuing supply of food, and were performed to promote those spirits which controlled this aspect of the universe. Masks, an important but not indispensable factor in dances, usually belonged to one spirit, song and dance. Height: 25.4 cm.

Donor:
Mrs. G.R. Hookham, 1939
Cat. No. AB 167

Wallet.
Inuit - Attu, date unknown

Fine basketry such as this is made by the native peoples of the Aleutian Islands off the south-west coast of Alaska. This wallet consists of two flat pouches, one fitting inside the other. It is woven of sea grass, using the technique of twining, and has three central design fields of false embroidery done in salmon-coloured and white silk thread. Length (when closed): 11.4 cm.

Donation/Transfer:
Edward and Mary Lipsett, 1941/1971
Cat. No. AB 221 a, b.

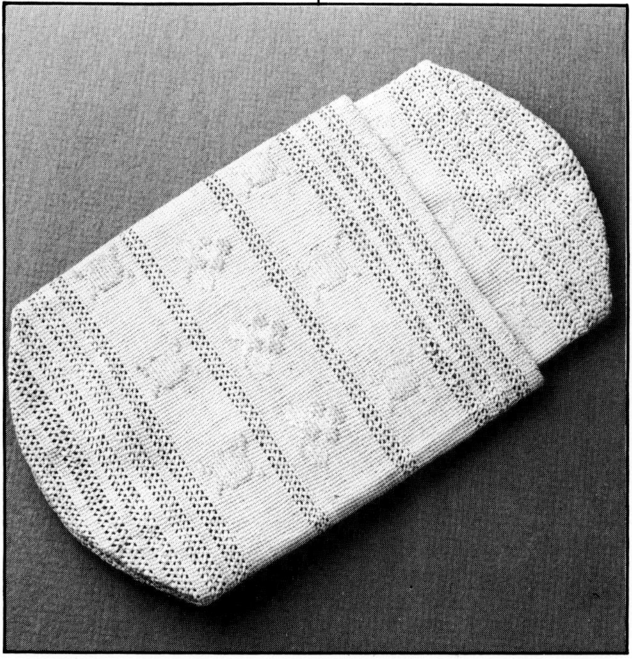

Sculpture.
Inuit, 20th Century.

This sculpture is carved from stone in the form of a woman. It dates from the mid-20th Century, the period which marked the widespread appearance of contemporary Inuit art in stone sculpture and prints. In 1948, supported by the Canadian government, the Hudson's Bay Company, and the Anglican Church, James Houston, an Ontario artist, began a programme to promote the creation and help the purchase and distribution of works of art by local Inuit in the Povungnetuk area. The results of Houston's efforts were the immediate and remarkable success of this new art, first in Montreal and throughout Canada, then abroad. Height: 33 cm.

Donor:
Art, Historical and Scientific Association, 1964
Cat. No. AB 47

Moccasins.

Plains – Possibly Blood or Western Sioux, date unknown.

The upper parts of these moccasins are made from buckskin, covered with blue, white and red glass seed beads sewn on by the lazy-stitch method, and are attached to rawhide soles. There is a red and white calico binding at the tops, and a cord wrapped in porcupine quill around the ankles. Cone-shaped metal pieces and red feathers are attached to the ends of the long forked beaded tongues. Elaborate beading such as this was important to individual pride and family reputation, and was therefore a form of status symbol. Length: 30.5 cm.

Donor:
Mr. Percy Bently, 1948
Cat. No. AF 1

Basket.

Southwest – Pima, date unknown

This coiled, shallow-bowl type basket is constructed from willow and devil's claw fibre on a warp of cattail stems. The geometric design, effected by the darker devil's claw fibre, is that of the Pima "fret". Appearing in many variations, it is the oldest and most commonly used basket design of these people. Baskets such as this one are often referred to as wheat baskets, since they are used in winnowing the grain on the threshing floor or for catching the ground wheat. Diameter: 55.8 cm.

Donation/transfer:
Edward and Mary Lipsett, 1941/1971
Cat. No. AI 12

Jar.

Southwest – San Ildefonso Pueblo, 19th Century

This jar is made of buff earthenware and is of a coiled construction. It is slip-painted, with black and red-brown geometric designs on a cream-coloured background, and then burnished. The jar may well be an early example of what has become a craft renaissance. In fact, since c. 1915, pottery has become economically important to these people. With the exception of ceremonial bowls, it is made solely for sale to tourists. Diameter: 50.8 cm.

Donor:
Professor Charles Hill-Tout, 1910
Cat. No. AI 5

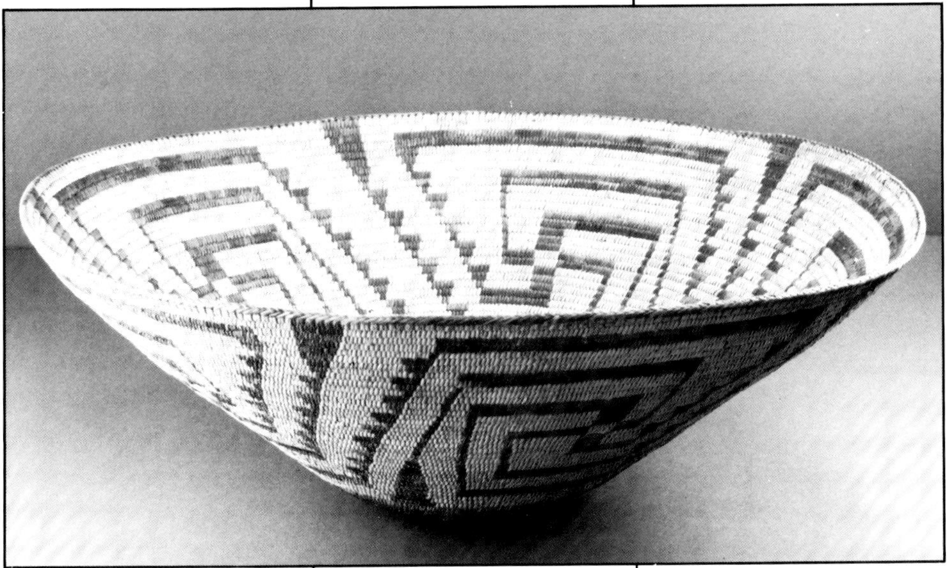

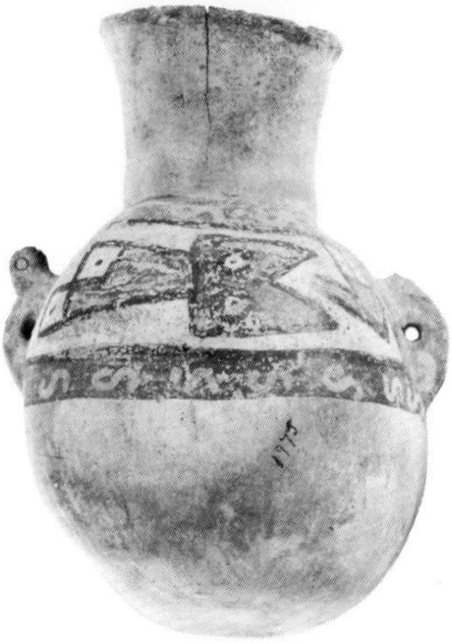

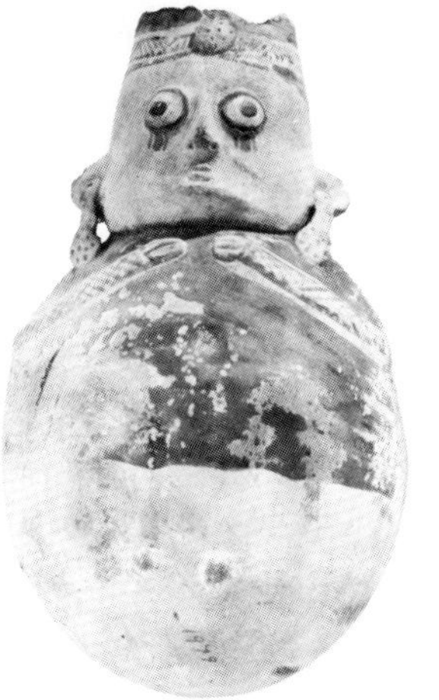

Funerary Vessels.
Peru, South America, c. 1000 A.D. — c. 1400 A.D.

The museum's small collection of archaeological material from South America consists mainly of ceramics, some of which are shown here. These polychrome pottery vessels functioned as containers for "chicha", a corn-brew offering which was placed in temples with the dead. The vessel on the left, c. 1000 A.D., belongs to a period characterized by designs which imitate those found on textiles. A favourite motif was the fish. The other two vessels are dated c. 1400 A.D. and belong to the late Chancay type of pottery. A typical ceramic type of this culture exhibiting a predilection for modelling is illustrated by the centre piece, a rather crude effigy vessel decorated in black and white. Heights (left to right) 26 cm, 26.6 cm, 24.2 cm.

Donor: Miss W. Crump, 1911
Cat. Nos. (left to right) QBD 20, QBD 19, QBD 22

Vessels.
Peru, South America, c. 1400 A.D. — 1532 A.D.

The funerary vessel on the left, c. 1400 A.D., was modelled in the form of a donkey carrying a beaker-shaped jar on its back. The whistling jar on the right, 1470-1532 A.D., has two compartments, one spherical and the other in the form of a human figure. When liquid was decanted a whistling sound would emerge. Heights (left) 17.8 cm (right) 15.9 cm.

Donors:
(left) Miss W. Crump, 1911
(right) Miss E. Harrop, 1938
Cat. Nos. (left) QBD 21, (right) QBD 23

Shrunken Human Head,
Tsantsa.
Ecuador, Jivaro, Date unknown.

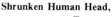

The Jivaro launch head-taking raids against groups that "speak differently" or "live far away". During the return homeward, the head-takers shrink the skins peeled from the heads. The process involves boiling the skin in water, rolling heated pebbles inside, filling with hot sand, massaging, drying, blackening the skin with charcoal, and lashing the lips together. The *tsantsa* (shrunken head trophy) takes approximately six days to prepare. Home-coming feasts allow the head-taker, as an accomplished warrior and generous host, to acquire prestige, friendship and obligations. The practice of shrinking human heads is related to the Jivaro concept of the *muisak* or avenging soul, and the ritual associated with the *tsantsa* is an effort to thwart the *muisak* in its mission of vengeance. The completion of the head-shrinking process forces the *muisak*, hovering alongside the retreating raiding expedition, to enter the *tsantsa*. Consequently, the *tsantsa* is prepared as quickly as possible following the raid. Height (head only): 8.9 cm.

Donor:
Mrs. W.S. Buttar, 1941
Cat. No. BD 113

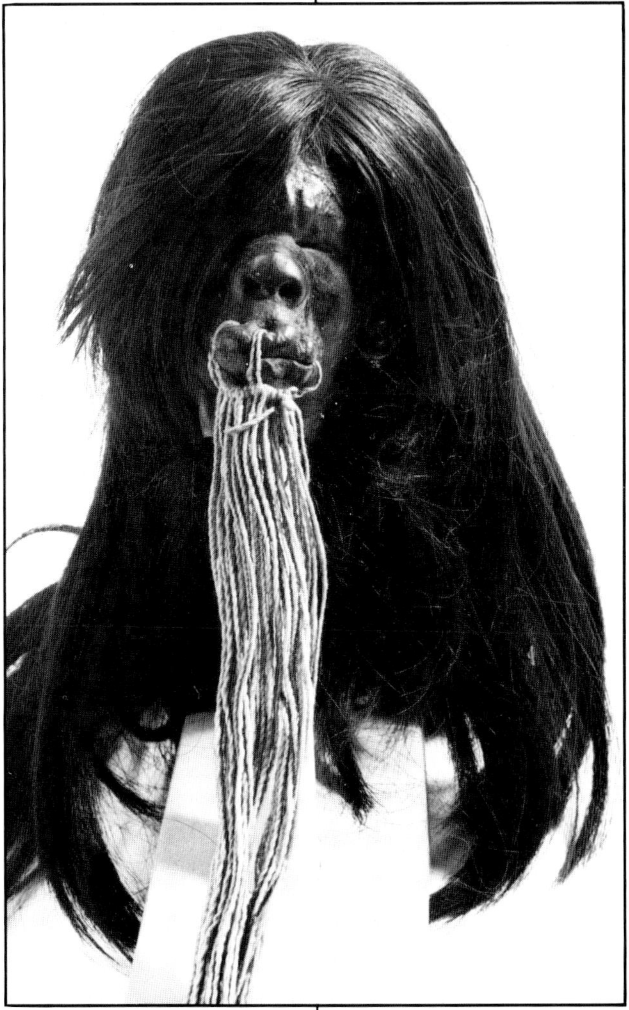

Bowl.
Bolivia, Aymara, Date unknown

This unpainted bowl with one pair of yolked bullocks in its centre and two handles, one at each side, is totally carved from a single piece of wood. It is badly cracked and crudely mended with silver. Recorded as a fiesta harvest bowl, it is reported to have been used to hold corn liquor. This piece is one of ten similar bowls from the same area held in the museum's collection. Diameter: 24.1 cm.

Donor:
Mrs. John Webster, 1957
Cat. No. BD 12

Bag.

Eastern Woodlands — Iroquois, date unknown

This shoulder bag is made of red flannel and decorated primarily with white, red, green, blue and black glass seed beads. Two beaded areas, the front centre panel of the pouch and the shoulder strap, are loom woven. In other areas, the beads are sewn on by the spot-stitch method. Additional decoration includes cotton-covered buttons above the pouch opening, and large glass beads hanging from the tab-like extensions at the bottom of the beaded front panel. According to the donors, bags such as this one were worn by men, especially by members of the Medicine Lodge Society, during ceremonials. After receiving a Salish basket in 1902, the Lipsetts' collection grew to some two thousand pieces, consisting primarily of North American Indian and Oriental artifacts. In 1941, part of the collection was presented to the City of Vancouver. From 1941 to 1971, it was housed at Exhibition Park, first in the old aquarium building, re-named the "Edward and Mary Lipsett Indian Museum", and from 1954, in the B.C. Building. In 1971, mainly through the efforts of Mrs. C.A. Ryan, daughter of the Lipsetts, the collection, numbering some 1100 pieces including this bag, was transferred to the Museum. Total length: 88.9 cm.

Donation/transfer: Edward and Mary Lipsett, 1941/1971
Cat. No. AG 83

Baskets.
California — Pomo, date unknown.

Both of these baskets are of a small coil-type construction. The one on the left is woven from willow and is decorated with woodpecker and quail feathers, clam shell, and glass seed beads. Similarly, the basket on the right is constructed of willow and sedge, with meadow lark, mallard duck and quail feather, clam and abalone shell decorations. Baskets such as these were made as special gifts and were considered great treasures. Diameters: (left) 8.9 cm; (right) 5.1 cm.

Donation/transfer: Edward and Mary Lipsett, 1941/1971
Cat. Nos. (left) AJ5, (right) AJ4.

Minerals.
America

The Grant Collection of minerals, purchased in 1910, was one of the Museum's first natural history acquisitions and contains hundreds of beautiful and rare crystal specimens.

Azurite. *Copper Queen Mine, Bisbee, Arizona*
Bright blue transparent or translucent crystals typify Azurite. It is commonly found in the oxidized zones of copper deposits, often in conjunction with malachite.

Herkimer Diamond (Quartz). *Herkimer County, New York, U.S.A.*
Quartz, one of the most important constituents of the earth's surface, is remarkable for its crystalline form. Its qualities give it common use as a gem stone, and depending on its colour it can be marketed as citrine, amethyst, onyx, carnelian or other semi-precious stones. The crystals from Herkimer County shown in the photo are of such colourless transparency as to be euphemistically called "diamonds".

Museum purchase, 1910

EUROPE

Minerals.
Europe

The museum's world-wide collection of minerals has been growing steadily since the early 1900's and has been a source of interest to both the museum visitor and the scholar. Shown here are a few of the European specimens.

1. **Sulphur.**
Girgienti, Sicily
Sulphur, a non-metallic chemical element also referred to as "brimstone" has been known from antiquity, and owing to its flammability was regarded by alchemists as the principle of combustion. It is often found in the proximity of volcanoes and in its purest form is a transparent or translucent yellow crystal.

2. **Fluorite.**
Cumberland, England

3. **Fluorite.**
Cornwall, England
Fluorite, or fluorspar is a native fluoride of calcium which derives its name from its use as a flux in metallurgy, its Latin root word *fluere* meaning "to flow". One of the most interesting characteristics of fluorite is its great variety of colours and samples may be white, yellow, green, blue, purple, or red. The mineral is used as an ornamental stone and in optical work and metal smelting, and as a source of the hydrofluoric acid used in the etching of glass.

4. **Bournonite.**
Liskeard, England
Bournonite, a mineral ore composed of lead, copper, antimony and sulphur, was named for Count J.L. de Bournon (1751-1825) who first described it scientifically in 1804. The ore often occurs in twin crystals reminiscent of cog wheels which gives it the common name "wheel ore". The mineral is opaque and has a brilliant metallic lustre with a lead-grey colour.

Donor:
1. Dr. Peter Bancroft, 1966
2, 3, 4. Museum Purchase, 1910

Evening Dress.
England, 1878-1880

Truly, one of the most spectacular garments in the Museum's collection, this evening dress illustrates the lavish ornamentation so fashionable in the late 1870's. The bodice cut and the white silk fabric decorated with small floral sprigs are meant to be reminiscent of styles popular in the mid 18th century. The slender skirt is tied back to create a tight sheath arranged in a bustle of cascading folds and puffs. Total back length 203 cm.

Donor:
Mrs. E.C. Glaspie, 1968
Cat. No. H972.149.2

Toby Jugs.
Staffordshire, England, c. 1950

The Toby Jug was inspired by an engraving dated 1761 of a character called 'Toby Fillpot' who drank, so the story goes, 2,000 gallons of beer from a silver tankard. Over the years many variations have appeared. After the First World War, for example, a series of eleven famous personages on the Allied side were modelled; five of these are shown here. From left to right: Admiral Beatty, Marshal Foch, King George V, President Wilson and Field Marshal Haig. They form part of the series of donations given by R. Wilson Galbraith, the man principally responsible for laying the foundations of the Vancouver Museum's European Decorative Arts collection. Average height 30 cm.

Donor:
R. Wilson Galbraith, 1961
Cat. Nos. (left to right)
CA 488, CA 483, CA 480, CA 481, CA 485

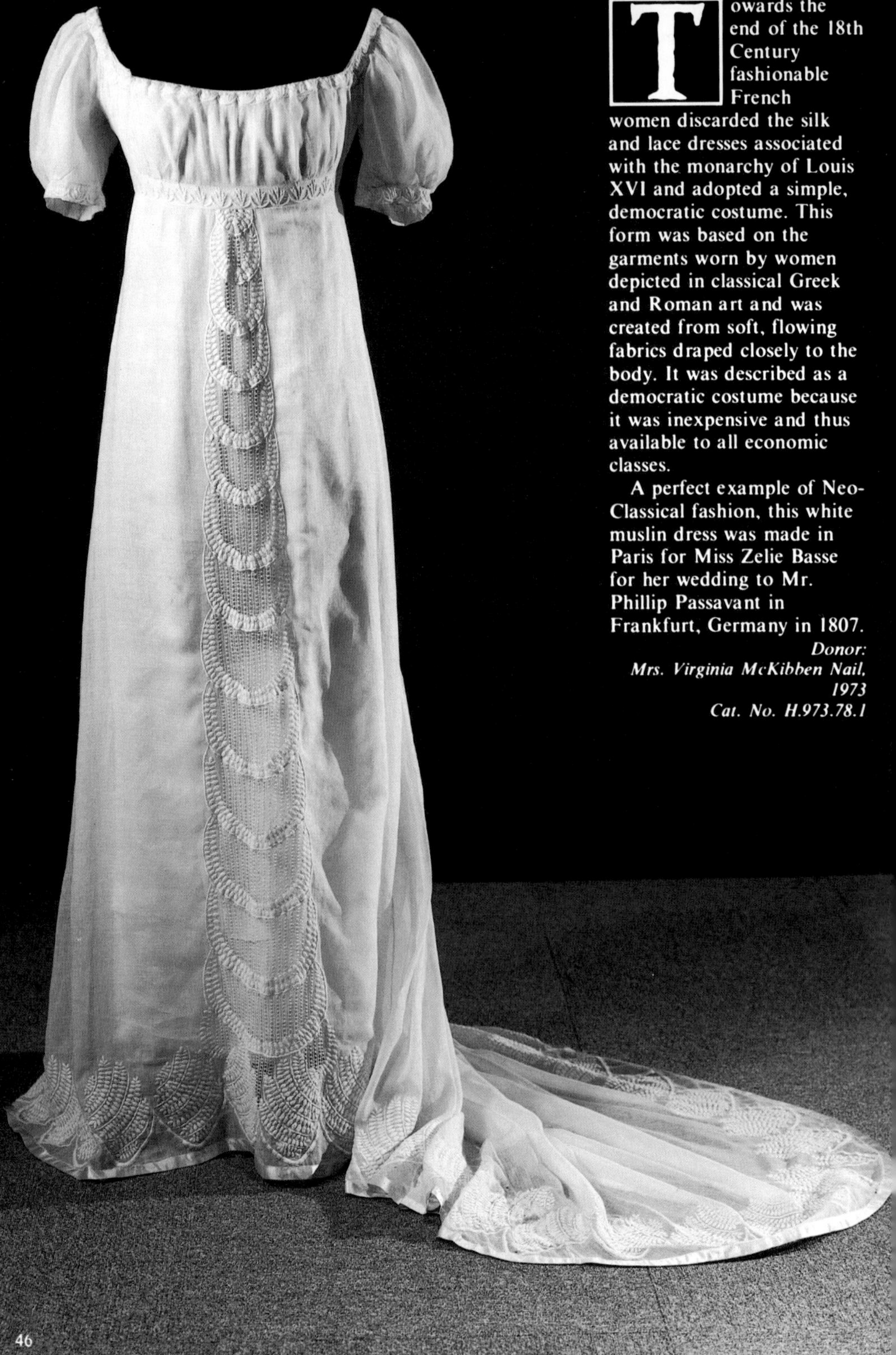

Wedding Dress.
France, 1807

Towards the end of the 18th Century fashionable French women discarded the silk and lace dresses associated with the monarchy of Louis XVI and adopted a simple, democratic costume. This form was based on the garments worn by women depicted in classical Greek and Roman art and was created from soft, flowing fabrics draped closely to the body. It was described as a democratic costume because it was inexpensive and thus available to all economic classes.

A perfect example of Neo-Classical fashion, this white muslin dress was made in Paris for Miss Zelie Basse for her wedding to Mr. Phillip Passavant in Frankfurt, Germany in 1807.

Donor:
Mrs. Virginia McKibben Nail, 1973
Cat. No. H.973.78.1

Figurine.
Derby, England, c. 1790

Porcelain figurines were made to adorn the tables, mantles and cabinets of the wealthy and were often superb examples of the modeller's art. This young lady is made of soft-paste porcelain, an imitation invented as a substitute before the secret of hard-paste or true porcelain was discovered. Soft-paste porcelain was made from a wide variety of materials, mainly white clay and ground glass, and was produced in England during the eighteenth century. Because it often required three separate firings, losses in the kilns were considerable so production on a commercial scale was rarely achieved. The subsequent rarity of soft-paste porcelain is one of the reasons it is often preferred by collectors.
Height 17.5 cm.

Donor:
Anonymous, 1981
Cat. No. H976.60.19

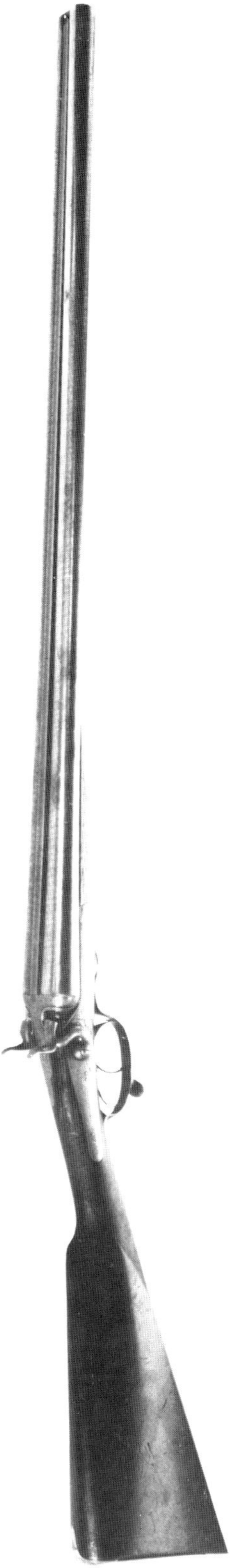

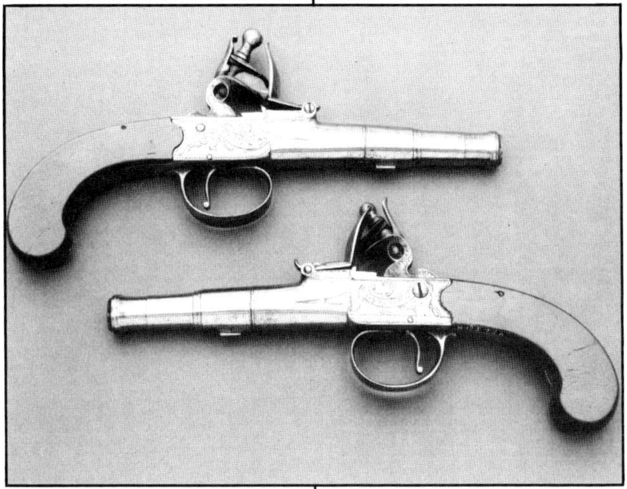

Shotgun.
England, c. 1880

This very fine sporting gun, a double-barreled, 12-gauge shotgun was made by Boss & Co., London. The company was founded in 1832, and the excellent quality of their guns, cartridges and shells has kept them in business to the present day.

This particular weapon is remarkable for its intricately engraved ornamentation and the beautiful swirling patterns in the damascene steel of the barrels. The gun opens by means of a lever in front of the trigger, and takes down by means of a lever in front of the forestock. Length 119 cm.

Donor:
H.G. Abbott (Estate), 1974
Cat. No. H974.79.3

Pocket Pistols.
England, late 18th Century

Part of a large donation, this pair of box-lock, turn-off pistols is unique in the museum's collection of firearms. The pistols are fitted with cannon barrels of circular cross-section and smooth bore. The barrels are in three stages with moulded girdles between, ending in a muzzle ring. Length 23 cm.

Donor:
David H. Molson, 1973
Cat. No. H973.73.5, .6

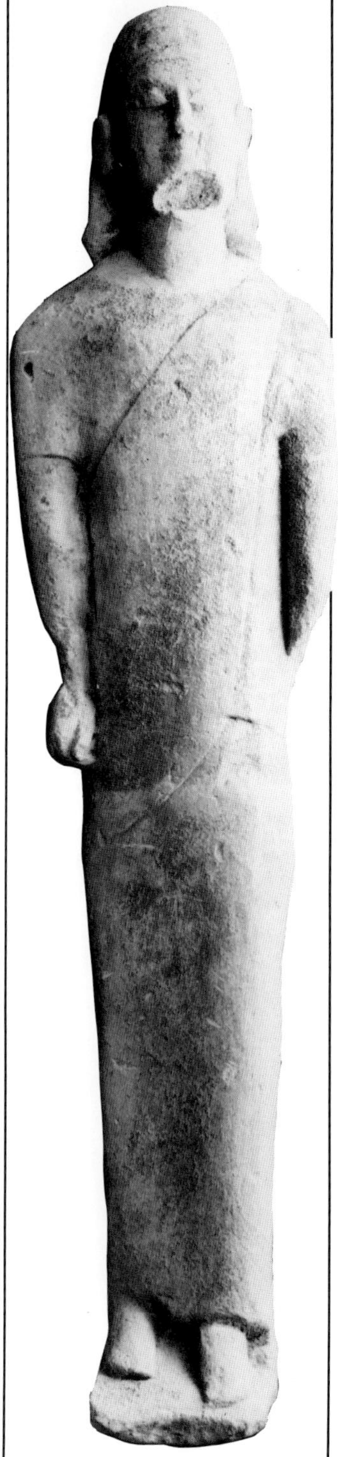

Statuette.
Greece, c. mid 6th Century B.C.

This limestone statuette of a youth *kouros* is executed in the Cypro-Egyptian style. The figure is wearing a plain chiton with a himation pulled diagonally across his chest. His facial features are treated in a cursory fashion showing traces of an archaic smile. The arms are stretched downwards with fists clenched and the left leg is slightly advanced. The back of the figure is uncarved, indicating that it was intended to be viewed only from the front.
Height 58.5 cm.

Donor:
British Museum, 1934
Cat. No. QCE 40

Figurine.
Staffordshire, England, c. 1845

Staffordshire pottery figures have a range and diversity to be found nowhere else in the world. Royalty, statesmen, actors, sportsmen and criminals were among the favourite subjects and were portrayed in every manner—with humor, naivete, deep respect and caricature.

These porcelain female figures were said to be two sisters who were Music Hall stars, their stage name being 'The Alphington Ponies'. They were illustrated on contemporary sheet music and are shown here carrying green umbrellas and wearing green hats, and pale yellow coats over white skirts. Height 12 cm.

Donor:
R. Wilson Galbraith, 1966
Cat. No. H.972.426.166

Salt Cellar.
Plymouth, England, 1770

This moulded salt cellar, one of a pair, is manufactured in the shape of a sea-shell resting on a number of smaller shells. It is made of hard-paste or true porcelain, a combination of kaolin and chinastone which when fired at a high temperature fuse to a glassy matrix. Hard-paste porcelain was first made in China in the seventh or eighth century AD but the process eluded English factories until 1768 when it was independently discovered by William Cookworthy. The Plymouth porcelain factory was the first to make hard-paste porcelain and among their wares can be found salt cellars of the type illustrated here. Length 12.7 cm.

Donor:
Mr. R. Wilson Galbraith, 1966
Cat. No. H.976.426.106

Plates.
Royal Doulton, England, c. 1905

These plates are selected from a set decorated with images from Charles Dana Gibson's portfolio of drawings, "A Widow and Her Friends". They were produced by the Royal Doulton Company, England, exclusively for the American market. Mr. Gibson, an American artist and illustrator was well known as the creator of the Gibson Girl, the heroine of "A Widow and Her Friends". She became the feminine ideal of turn-of-the-century America, was shown at various occupations, and it is said that her influence touched women in all walks of life. Each plate bears Gibson's signature in under-glaze black superimposed on bright blue petals. The same blue is used for the wide stylized leaf border. Diameter 26.7 cm.

Donor:
Mr. J. Gerald Bradley (Estate), 1978
Cat. No. H.978.17.1(a-r)

Longcase clock.
England, early 18th century

Longcase is the correct name for the Grandfather or Grandmother clock. This eighteenth century example has a red japanned case decorated in chinoiserie, a western imitation of Chinese art. The clock movement has a painted dial which is 75-100 years later than the case. The name "Finnemore" is stamped into the back of the brass plate portion of the movement. This clock was originally part of the furnishings in the Vancouver mansion of General (later Senator) Alexander Duncan McRae. The mansion is now the home of the University Women's Club. Because of its close historical ties to Vancouver, this clock has been certified as a National Treasure under the Cultural Property Export and Import Act. Height 243.4 cm.

Donor:
Mr. R.K. Ward, 1978
Cat. No. H979.9.1

Chair.
England, c. 1805-1815

This 'Trafalgar chair', so called because it came from the 'Trafalgar Workshops', named as a tribute to Lord Nelson, is one of the most distinctive forms of furniture developed during the Regency. It is characterized by concave 'sabre' or 'scimitar' front legs, rounded knees and rope cresting — an allusion to the victories at sea of the British fleet. Height 82.5 cm.

Donor:
Mr. R.K. Ward, 1980
Cat. No. 1980.132.68

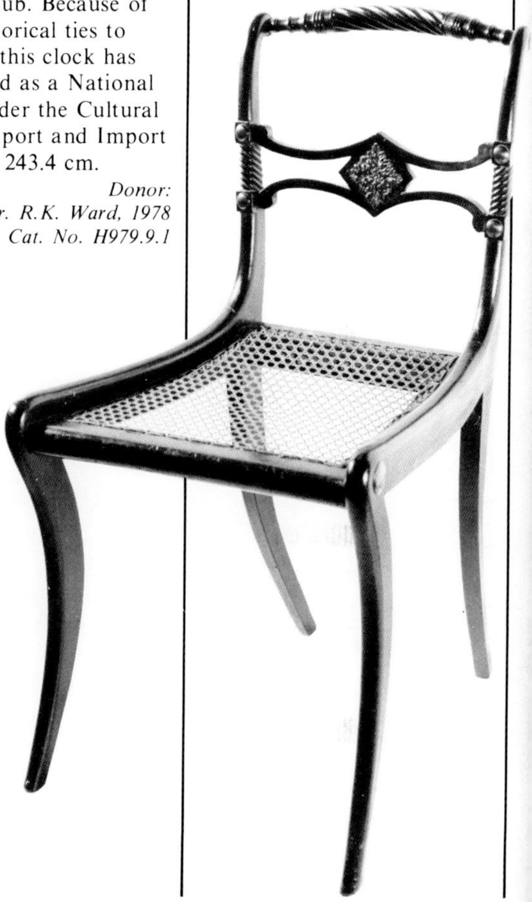

Box and lid.
France, c. 1930

This box decorated with the nude figure of a female came from the Lalique workshop. Rene Lalique (1860-1945) was famous both as a jeweller and a glass-maker. He was fascinated by the mystic colour of moonstones and it is this cloudy pale blue opalescence for which his glass is renowned. His creations were favourites of European Royalty. He designed an entire crystal table service for King George VI and made glasses engraved with the crest of the Duke of Windsor. The company remains a family concern and the firm currently offers more than 800 creations for sale.
Height 14.5 cm.

Donor:
Mr. R. Wilson Galbraith, 1966
Cat. No. H972.426.17 a, b

Wine glasses.
England, c. 1750-1780

The majority of surviving eighteenth century English glasses takes the form of drinking vessels, above all, wine glasses. When George Ravenscroft introduced oxide of lead to the manufacturing of glass in 1675 a solid heavy glass was produced which diffused light with a brilliance enhanced by the darkness of its shadows. Glass shapes were simple and usually undecorated, but their weight became a disadvantage when the Excise Tax of 1745 levied a duty on glass by weight. This encouraged glass-makers to produce lighter and smaller glasses. Sometimes, the bowls were engraved, but probably the most distinguishing feature was to be found in the stem, where groups of air bubbles were drawn out to form multiple spirals of air-lines. These features can be seen in the examples illustrated. In many ways, these superb glasses were the product of an economic necessity that challenged the ingenuity of the artist. Heights (left to right) 15.5 cm, 14.0 cm, 18.5 cm, 15.3 cm.

Donor:
Mr. R. Wilson Galbraith, 1966
Cat. Nos. (left to right)
H972.426.200, H972.426.201, H972.426.199, H972.426.203

Tea kettle with stand.
Elkington & Co., Birmingham, or Sheffield, England, c. 1890-1910

This tea kettle is electro-plated nickel silver, a process discovered by a Rotherham Engineer in 1844. It is decorated in a revival of the Rococo style which was very popular during the late nineteenth, early twentieth century. The idea of covering a base metal with a thin coating of precious metal was not new. From antiquity, base metal had been covered in various ways with a precious metal but this was never entirely satisfactory. The introduction of nickel silver and the process of electro-plating provided an acceptable article at far less cost, thus making silver objects available to a wide range of economic classes. Elkington & Co., the original patentees of electro-plated nickel silver, were based in Birmingham and led the field in producing replicas of solid silver originals. Height 32 cm.

Donor: Brigadier General F.W.E. Burnham, 1955
Cat. No. H971.282.1 a-c

Toy Theatre.
German or Bavarian, 1875-1900

At the end of the 18th century, the invention of lithography made it possible to produce large numbers of printed paper goods and novelties economically. Amongst the novelties especially created for the amusement and education of children, were toys such as this theatre. German printers in particular excelled at creating detailed, colourful designs which they exported successfully all over the world. The theatre illustrated can be dismantled and folded neatly into the wooden stage. The scenery is printed on both sides to make it reversible and there are sets of characters for "The Mikado", "Robinson Crusoe" and "Faust"(?). Height: 79 cm.

Museum Purchase: 1973
Cat. No. H973.134.1

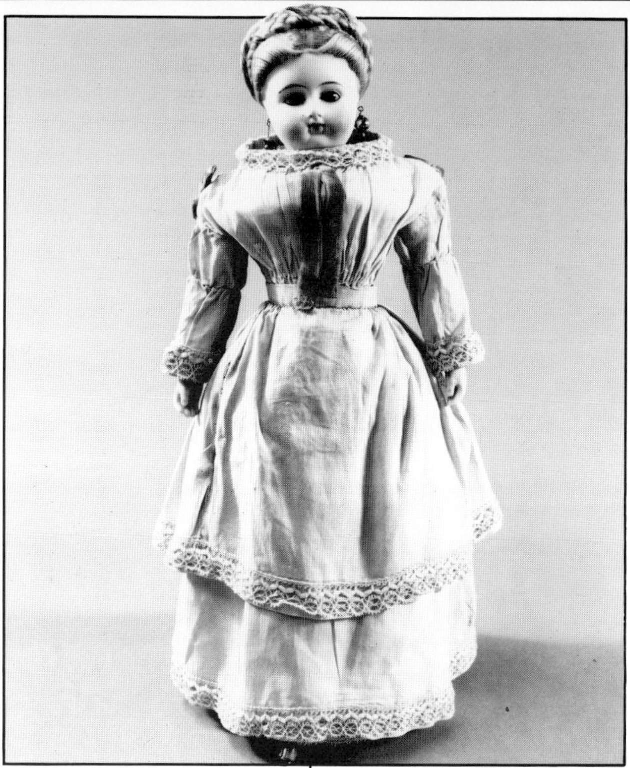

Doll.
German (?), c. 1845-1855

The Museum is the proud possessor of a collection of over three hundred dolls spanning the time period of c. 1750-c. 1950. Many of the dolls were collected for their great age and rarity, and others for their fame or their nostalgic value.

Here we show a beautiful bisque-headed adult doll dressed in her original flounced gown of fine mauve linen. Her blonde hair is moulded and her features are delicately painted in natural colours. Her body is white kid leather and her hands and boots are painted bisque. Her height is 33 cm. and she bears no maker's mark.

Donor:
Mrs. James Spelay, 1968
Cat. No. H972.194.2

Doll.
England, 1850's

This doll is a product of the most famous of all English toy manufacturers, the Montanari family of London. This family created much excitement at the Great Exhibition in 1851, where they were most notable for their work with finely tinted beeswax, a medium which gave their dolls a lifelike, translucent complexion. The example shown here was presented to the Museum with her complete wardrobe, although she is illustrated in only her undergarments. Her head, hands and feet are wax over papier mache. Her wig is of human hair and her body is fabric. Her overall length is 80 cm.

Donor:
Miss E. Gooding, 1936
Cat. No. H973.157.1

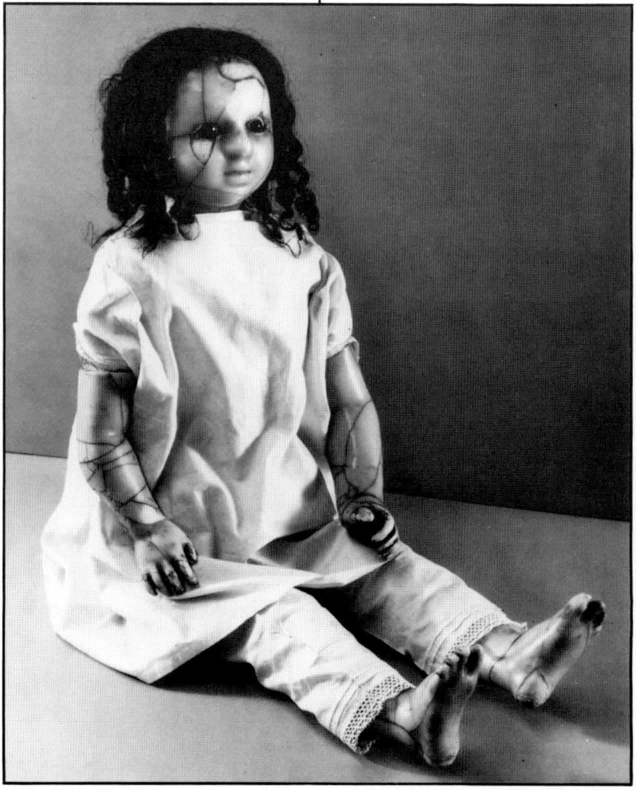

Doll.
France, 1860-1870

The Empress Eugenie, wife of Napoleon III of France, was known as one of the most beautiful women in Europe and was certainly one of the most influential figures of fashion. Her pale blonde hair and wistful expression were copied by women everywhere, and this imitation was carried over into the world of small children and their dolls.

The beautiful doll shown here has bisque head and hands and is intended to be a portrait of the Empress. The body is not labelled, but one shoe is marked, "Mode de Paris, A.P.".. She is 43 cm. tall and is shown wearing one of her many dresses ranging in date from c. 1860 through to c. 1905.

Donor:
Mrs. Esther Harland, 1975
Cat. No. H975.57.1

Shawl.
Belgian, c. 1855-1870

The Russian Crown presented this fine example of *"point de gaze"* needle lace to the donor when she married a British Military Attache appointed to the Imperial Russian Court. The shawl is completely made by hand, using linen thread and a needle to weave and knot the pattern together. The varieties of flowers and foliage are remarkably lifelike and their beauty is intended to be displayed against the large, hooped skirt of an evening dress. Width 258 cm.

Donor:
Mrs. S. Porteus, 1932
Cat. No. H977.391.1

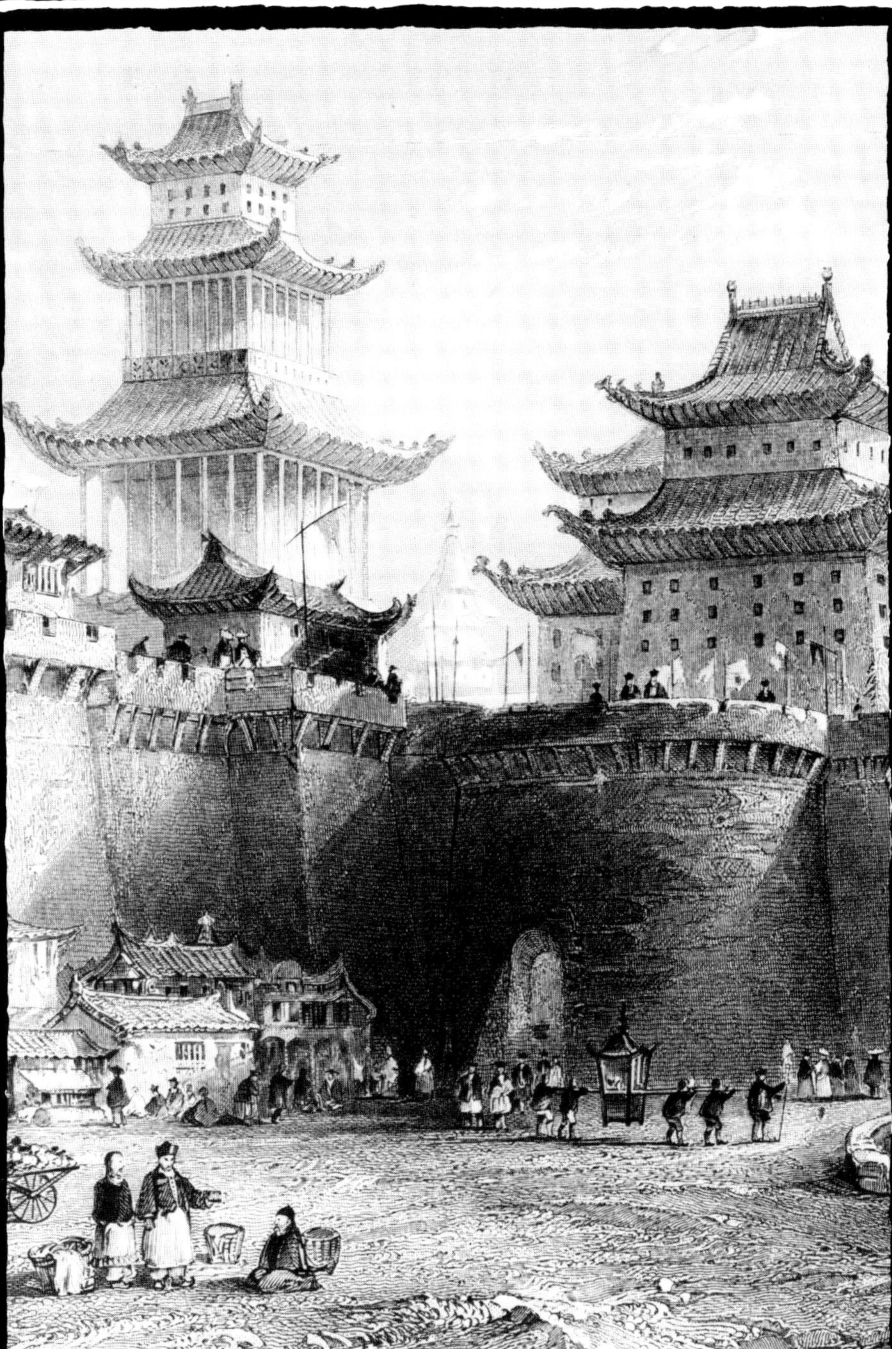

A·S·I·A

Bowl.
Japan, late 19th century

This bowl is marked "Jungin" (pure silver) and "Bigyoku". Although it is richly decorated with an overall design of chrysanthemums, a traditional Japanese motif, its shape is reminiscent of western traditions. Silver has never been abundant in Japan and refining methods were so wasteful that silver was employed chiefly in inlays and in the much used alloy *shibuichi*. It was perhaps the potential western market that encouraged craftsmen to pay more attention to silver, and to produce fine examples such as illustrated here. Width 30.6 cm.

Donors:
Reverend H. P. Brown and Bruce Brown, 1980
Cat. No. DB 771

Stibnite.
Ochinakawa, Japan.

Stibnite, the most important ore of antimony, was used by the Ancients as a cosmetic powder to darken the area around the eyes to make them appear larger. In modern times, antimony is used in printer's type, Britannia metal and in medicines. In large doses, the mineral is poisonous.

Stibnite is widely distributed but not in abundance, and the specimen shown is from the deposit famous for producing the largest and finest crystals in the world.

Museum Purchase, 1910

Dolls.
Japan.

The custom of celebrating the Dolls' Festival, *hinamatsuri,* originated in the middle of the Edo Period (1615-1867). Timed to coincide with the blooming of the peach tree, ceremonial dolls, not the everyday playthings of children, were displayed in a prescribed tiered arrangement. The highest tier was occupied by the Emperor and Empress, the second tier by court ladies, and the third and fourth tiers by court attendants and musicians. The attention to detail can be seen in the delicately modelled porcelain heads and hands, and the carefully reproduced costumes of the musicians illustrated here. Heights 9.5 cm.

Museum purchase, 1958
Cat. Nos. DB 664, DB 662, DB 673

Helmet, *Kabuto,* and Face Guard, *Mempo*. *Japan.*

The armour of Japan, elaborate in detail, differed so strongly from its Western counterpart that it was often thought to be impractical for fighting and suitable only for ceremonial occasions. However, Japanese armour was as carefully designed for its defensive role as the Japanese sword was for attack. The complexity of the armour is illustrated by the helmet and face mask shown here. The helmet consists of a bowl with a small peak riveted to the front. Attached to the peak is a socket which would have received the owner's crest. The neck guard is made of five lames laced together with silk cords and trimmed with fur. The face guard with its detachable nose protects the face below the eyes; under the chin hangs a neck guard of five lacquered lames, to protect the neck. The face guard was also an important means of fastening the helmet to the wearer. A cord was laced from rings on the helmet to fastenings on the mempo and tied under the chin of the latter.

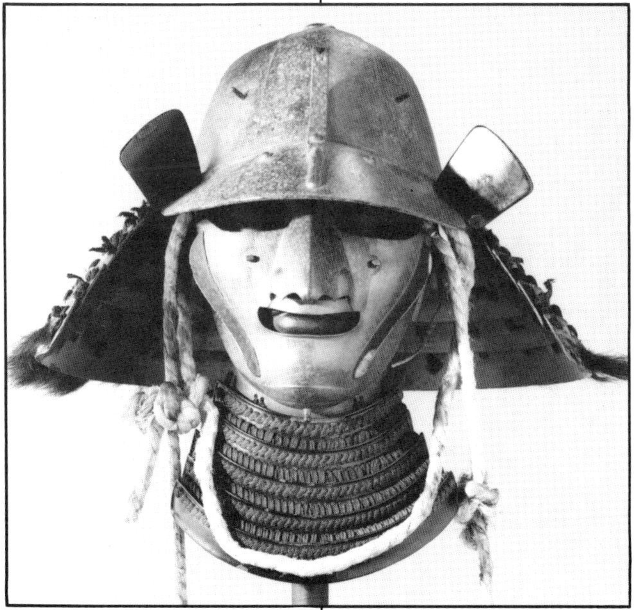

Height (helmet) 22.8 cm.
Height (face guard) 22.2 cm.

Donor:
Captain Henry Pybus, 1913
Cat. Nos. (Helmet) DB 114
(Face guard) DB 111

Tsuba.
Japan, 17th-19th century.

The Japanese sword guard, or *tsuba,* was originally a simple cross-bar, usually made of iron with the sole function of protecting the wielder's hand. The shape of the *tsuba* gradually developed into circular, oval, quatrefoil, etc., averaging 7 cm in diameter with a wedge-shaped opening at its centre to take the characteristically wide tang or handle portion of the blade. With the advent of Buddhist thought and idealism as propagated by the Zen sect, particularly in the 15th-16th Centuries, the minor arts, especially metalworking, were elevated. This gave an impetus to the decoration of the *tsuba.* The previously simple designs increased in complexity and utilized the more precious metals. The use of silver, gold, bronze, brass, copper and copper alloys became widespread and the techniques employed in their use became more sophisticated. The inspiration for the designs found on *tsuba* came from many sources: episodes from the lives of Japanese poets or warriors, Buddhist symbolism, battle scenes from history and mythology, sages and magicians. The repertory of subjects and themes was almost endless. Such superb skill was expended by great artists in working the metals and in their remarkable manipulation of design, that the Japanese refer to the best work as "painting with the chisel". The Vancouver Museum is extremely fortunate in having a collection of over four hundred *tsuba,* a few of which are illustrated here.

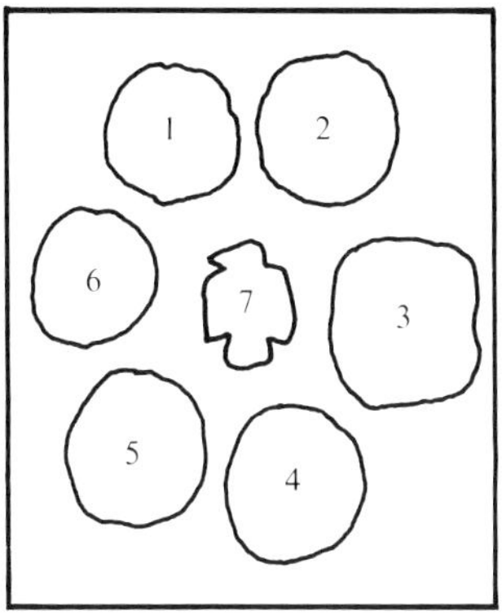

1/2. Dai-sho (pair). Copper alloy with gold. Design: bamboo grass. Unsigned, 18th century
3. Brass with copper and iron. Design: eagle and two monkeys on rocks. Signed: Masatusume, 19th century.
4. Copper alloy. Design: Buddhist swastika (Manji). Signed: Oshima Shigeyoshi, 18th century
5. Iron with copper and gold inlay. Design: two armed warriors and strong man. Signed: Soheishi Niudo Soten, 17th or early 18th century
6. Copper alloy. Design: fish and prawns. Unsigned. 18th or 19th century
7. Iron. Design: silhouette of bird. Unsigned. Date unknown

Cat. Nos. 1/2. DB 455 ab, 3. DB 457, 4. DB 448, 5. DB 462, 6. DB 458, 7. DB 186
Donors:
(1-6) Captain James Inman, 1945
(7) Captain Henry Pybus, 1900

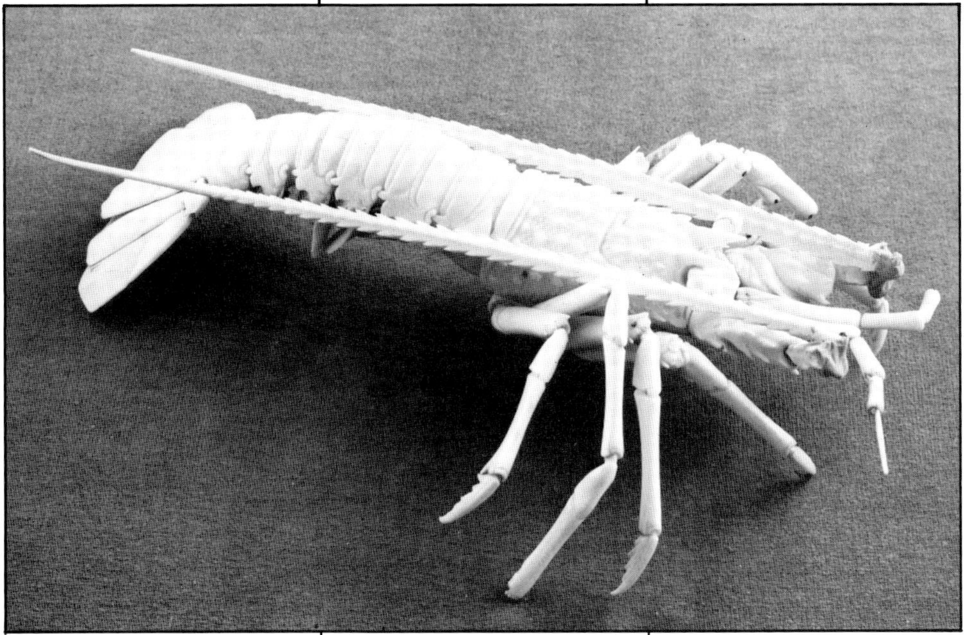

Carving, *Okimono.*
Japan, Meiji period (1868-1912)

Due to the separation of Buddhism and Shinto and the subsequent destruction of shrines and sculpture, the early Meiji period was a difficult time for the carver of religious themes. He was forced to turn to carving *netsuke* and *okimono*. Although ivory *okimono* were made before the Meiji period, that was considered their heyday. As their popularity grew the subject matter of these *okimono* was designed to please the taste of the Western collectors. The result was a proliferation of genre figures, flowering plants, and animals. The *okimono* illustrated here is of wandering showmen with their monkey troupe. Monkeys were a favourite subject because the carver could exhibit his skill in the portrayal of their downy coats. However, such attention to detail has not prevented the carver from capturing the mobility and playfulness of this charming scene. Height 14.5 cm.

Donors:
Edward and Mary Lipsett, 1949
Cat. No. DA 265

Carving, *Okimono.*
Japan, Meiji period (1868-1912)

This *okimono* of a crayfish is a fine example of multiple piece construction, a skill perfected by the carvers of the Meiji period. Each section of the body is separately carved and then assembled. The carver's knowledge of anatomy becomes apparent when the articulated body is set in motion. The movements of a live crayfish can be reproduced faithfully, thus completing the illusion of the natural form.
Length 25.5 cm

Donors:
Edward and Mary Lipsett, 1949
Cat. No. DB 655

Sculpture.
China, date unknown.

This crudely modelled ceramic sculpture has been the object of much speculation. It is believed to have originated in the Honan Province and has been referred to as a "burial brick". It is doubtful, however, that it was ever used as a funerary object. The bed-like sofa, *kang,* reminiscent of late Ming furniture, contains a reclining male figure covered with a floral decorated blanket. Seated on the edge is a female figure wearing a crown. Inscribed on the back of the sofa in Chinese script are the words "Woman kills husband". This would seem to refer to the legend of the Golden Lotus recorded in the 16th Century, which told the story of a woman who killed her husband so that she could marry her lover. The only other information available is that the sculpture was collected by the donor in the early 1900's. Width 28.5 cm.

Donor:
Mrs. E.M. Clark, 1946
Cat. No. DA 960

Roof Tile.
China, Ming (1364-1644)

This turquoise glazed pottery fish is a decorative ridge tile of the type associated with the roofs of Ming buildings — summer palaces, smaller temples and pagodas. Roofs were seen as major platforms of communication between Heaven and Earth, and roof tiles were expressions of popular beliefs and practices. The fish (a carp), was believed to be capable of transformation into a dragon if it successfully leaped the rapids of the Yellow River, which were known as the Dragon Gates in Chinese legend. The fish was also an amulet against danger to buildings from fire. Although roof tiles were never intended to be viewed at close range, the tile illustrated here bears scrutiny extremely well. Height 19.8 cm.

Donors:
Edward and Mary Lipsett, 1949
Cat. No. DA 448a

Vessel.

China, date unknown

This cast bronze vessel collected in Honan Province is fashioned in the shape of a three-legged toad. Many stories and superstitions have been connected with the toad, partly because of its strange appearance and also because of the length of its life span, which may extend to forty years. The three-legged toad of Chinese mythology is said to exist only in the moon, which it swallows during the eclipse. It has therefore come to be the emblem of the unattainable. Images of the toad are regarded as conducive to good fortune, and the three-legged toad is also the symbol of money-making. Height 23 cm.

Donor:
Mrs. E.M. Clark, 1946
Cat. No. DA 1083

Buddhist Lion.

China, 18th-19th century

This bronze vessel, probably an incense burner, is cast in the shape of a lion. The lion was not indigenous to China but was introduced in connection with Buddhism, figuring as the defender of law and protector of sacred buildings. He is usually represented *sejant* — seated — either with both forefeet on the ground, or with one raised in a menacing attitude. However, despite his bulging eyes and fierce countenance he is usually depicted with a beautifully curled mane, playing with a ball, *chu*. Height 30.5 cm.

Donor:
Mrs. E.M. Clark, 1946
Cat. No. DA 46

Informal Coat, *ch'ang fu*.
China, c. 1900

Two distinctly different styles of dress, Chinese and Manchu, existed and blended within the Ch'ing period (1644-1911). The Chinese style evolved from cloth construction dictated by the loom. For upper body garments, two lengths were brought over the shoulders and seamed at the back and sides below the armholes. This resulted in a straight unshaped shoulder, full sleeves and a centre front opening. The Manchu style derived from the shape of animal skins from which their garments were first constructed. A close fitting bodice conserved heat, as did the overlap of the left front extension, and tight sleeves ending in "horsehoof" cuffs protected the hands. By the end of the 19th Century some Manchu coats had adopted wide, straight sleeves more typical of Chinese robes, faced with contrasting fabric, which was turned back to form decorative cuffs. It is this later style of Manchu coat that is illustrated here. Length 137.2 cm.

Donors:
Mr. and Mrs. Gudewill, 1969
Cat. No. DA 1081

Image Coat.

China, 1875 - early 1900's

This richly decorated image coat, embroidered in gold thread, was probably used in the theatre or on a Temple idol. The overall design includes the five-clawed frontal dragon, which represents a high Imperial rank and is the embodiment of power and wisdom (see close-up). The Phoenix represents the Empress as well as beauty, goodness, the sun, abundant harvests, and reason in government. The foo dogs seen on the lower areas of the coat symbolize power and energy. This coat has been certified as a National Treasure of Canada under the Cultural Property Export and Import Act.
Length 134.6 cm.
Width (incl. arms) 210 cm.

Donors:
Mr. & Mrs. F. Reif, 1981
Cat. No. DA 1211

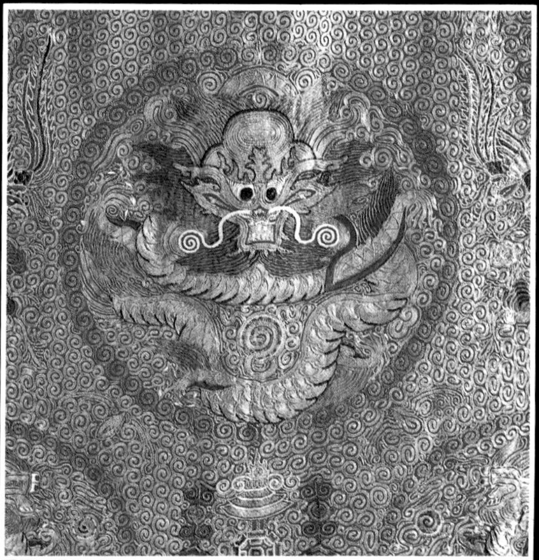

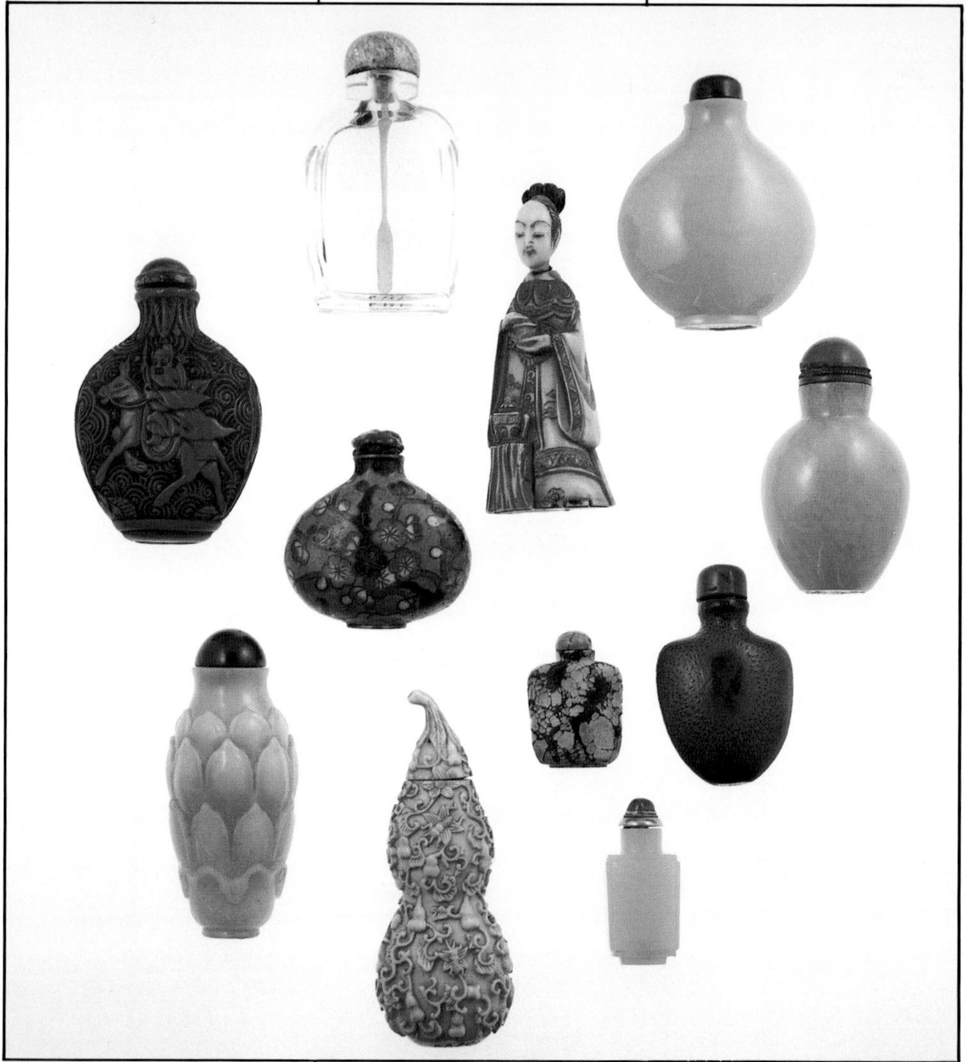

Snuff bottles.

China, late 18th - 19th century

Shown here is a selection from the museum's collection of of over 150 Chinese snuff bottles.

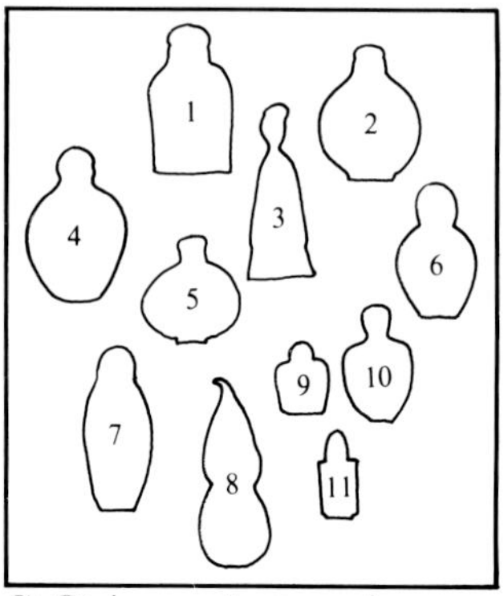

1) Crystal body, tourmaline stopper, early 19th century
2) Glass body and stopper, early 20th century
3) Ivory body and stopper, late 19th century
4) Cinnabar lacquer body, glass bead and brass stopper, early 19th century
5) Cloisonne body and stopper, late 18th - early 19th century
6) Jadeite body and stopper, late 19th - early 20th century
7) Glass body, late 19th century
8) Ivory body and stopper, early 19th century (?)
9) Turquoise body and stopper, early 20th century
10) Sharkskin (?) body, ceramic stopper, early 20th century
11) Jade body, ruby stopper, 19th century (?)

Donors:
Edward and Mary Lipsett, 1949
Cat. Nos. 1. DA 565, 2. DA 586, 3. DA 585, 4. DA 570, 5. DA 618, 6. DA 680, 7. DA 626, 8. DA 698, 9. DA 581, 10. DA 566, 11. DA 673.

Buddha.
Thailand, possibly 14th century

This Budda's hands are in *bhumispara mudra,* a gesture calling the earth to witness the supreme moment of the Enlightenment when Buddha overcame the forces of evil and began his mission to mankind on Earth. Since the attainment of individual enlightenment is an important goal of every Buddhist in Thailand, it is not surprising that this moment in Buddha's life has remained one of the most popular themes in Thai sculpture. Height 43.2 cm.

Donors:
Mrs. A.K. Briggs and family, 1925
Cat. No. DE 73

Books.
"The Illustration of a Thousand Shells", Y. Hirase

In 1931, Dr. Newton Drier presented his monumental collection of sea shells to the Vancouver Museum. Dr. Drier had travelled the world on his shell-hunting expeditions and, as Honorary Curator of Conchology, he remained associated with the Museum until his death in 1942.

Shown are three volumes of a set of four given by Dr. Drier to accompany his shell collection. Each illustration is finely detailed and meticulously hand-painted in water colours. The shell resting on the books is a *Spondylus,* or "Thorny Oyster", an inhabitant of warm, southern seas.

Donor:
Dr. Newton Drier, 1932.

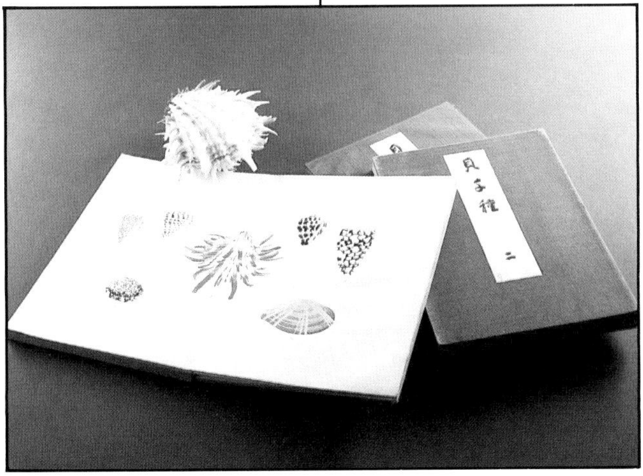

Bridal costume, *Hanayome-isho.*

Japan, 1980

This bridal costume is made of silk and the designs are worked with metallic threads. The flowers and birds symbolize happiness and longevity. The red kimono, *furisode,* with its long swinging sleeves, is typical of a style that has been worn by young girls and brides since the 17th Century. Because this is a bridal costume, the sash, *obi,* would be tied in an elaborate knot sometimes imitating the shape of butterfly wings. Traditionally the bride carried a knife in the *obi* so that, should anyone choose to question her honour, she would have the recourse to kill herself. The sumptuous overkimono, *uchikake,* had to be gathered up in order to walk and was usually associated with ceremonial occasions.

Donor:
Mr. Tomoji Ishi, 1981
Cat. No. DB 749-753

Costume Accessory.

Tibet, date unknown

Although Tibetan art is capable of great sophistication, it seldom totally severs its connection with the folk art of the semi-nomadic groups of the Northern territories. The link is well illustrated by this costume accessory, usually worn as part of an elaborate headdress, which achieves a rugged beauty with its combination of unworked pieces of turquoise and coarsely woven wool. Characteristic of northern Tibet, it would be worn on special occasions. Length 60.9 cm.

Museum Purchase, 1978
Cat. No. DE 380

AFRICA & OCEANIA

Minerals. Africa
(left) Cerussite.
Cerussite is an ore of lead and its name comes from the Latin for "white lead". The crystals are very dense and highly reflective and are usually colourless or pale grey or green.

(right) Mimetite
Mimetite is a rather rare secondary mineral that occurs in the oxidized parts of lead ores, especially those containing arsenic. The crystals are usually pale translucent yellow or brown.

(centre) Azurite
The deep azure blue of Azurite makes it easily identifiable in the field. Together with malachite it frequently indicates the pre sence of copper ore deposits.

Donor:
Tsumeb Copper Corporation, Tsumeb, Namibia

Sea Shells. *Oceania*

(top left) Murex Trocheli (Troschel's murex). Japan
Murex shells are often sculptured with delicate frills and spines.

(top right) Tridacna Squamosa (Frilled clam). Indo-Pacific to Australia
Specimens can be over twelve inches long.

(bottom left) Polymita Picta. Oriente, Cuba
This land snail can exhibit more than eleven thousand colour combinations.

(centre) Papuina Pulcherrina. South Pacific Islands
The Papuina Pulcherrina is valued for its flamboyant green.

(bottom right) Janthina Violacea
Found in warm areas, this snail manufactures a mucous float which enables it to swim at the surface.

Donor:
Dr. Newton Drier, 1932

Bowl.
Nigeria, Yoruba, date unknown

This piece comprises a lenticular shaped covered bowl atop a sculptured pedestal carved in the form of a rooster. The cover opens by means of a wood hinge to reveal a shallow bowl. It is carved from wood and painted in muted colours of black, turquoise, and red-brown. The donor's brother, W.A. Cowlin, collected the bowl c. 1900, during the time he was serving with the John Holt Co. in Lagos, Nigeria. Height: 22.8 cm. Diameter: 19 cm.

Donor:
Miss E.M. Cowlin, 1943
Cat. No. F 24

Beadwork.

(left) **Necklace,** *Natal, South Africa, Zulu, 19th Century.* Beads are strung around a bundle of fabric. Length: 78.7 cm.
Donor:
Mrs. C. Radermacher, 1947
Cat. No. F532

(right) **Headband.** *South Africa, possibly Zulu, date unknown.* Strands of beads hang from a thong. Length (maximum) 22.8 cm.
Donor:
M. Fitzgerald, 1958
Cat. No. F507

(bottom) **Belt,** *Kenya date unknown.* Loom-woven. Length: 73.6 cm.
Donor:
Mrs. R. Morrow, 1947
Cat. No. F603

Vessels.
Egypt, c. 3000 B.C.

These jars were excavated by Sir Flinders Petrie at Tarkham, tomb of King Zet, third king of the First Dynasty. Of all the crafts of which the Egyptians showed early mastery, stoneworking was perhaps the one most characteristic of their ancient civilization, and certainly it was the medium in which they achieved some of their finest and most memorable work. Alabaster (calcite) vessels, such as those illustrated here, have been recovered from many royal and private tombs. The nature of their beliefs about the after-life prompted the Egyptians to bury many possessions with the dead, and a high proportion of these have been preserved because of the dry climate. The translucent veining that occurs in alabaster is often cleverly used to enhance its appearance. The makers of these vessels are often credited with having developed techniques which are now lost to us. Heights (left to right) 23.5 cm, 44.0 cm, 32.5 cm.

Museum Purchase, 1920
Cat. Nos. QFA 139-42

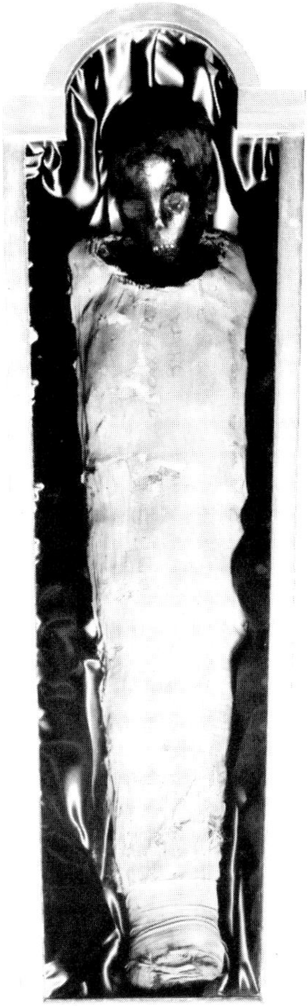

Mummified Adolescent Male.
Egypt, 1st-3rd century AD

This is the only mummy in the Museum's collection and, as such, has been the centre of much public attention. It was discovered in a rock-cut tomb approximately one mile from the Valley of the Tombs of the Kings, near Luxor. In 1915 the mummy was examined at the Egyptian Medical School in Cairo. At that time, it was identified as a little girl of high rank, and was dated from the sixth or fifth centuries B.C. It was displayed in Vancouver for about 30 years with the nickname "Diana". In 1951 the mummy was re-examined. A series of X-rays revealed that "Diana" was really a ten-year-old boy, and, further, that he had suffered serious injuries to the left side of the body which had probably caused his death. At this time, a translation of a Greek inscription on the wrappings over the chest of the mummy also suggested a new, later dating for it. The inscription was translated as "Penechates, son of Hatres" — two fairly common names in Egypt around the time of Christ. The style of lettering was not typical of the period of the original dating, and probably dates from the first to third centuries A.D. Length 104 cm.

Donor:
Dr. D.G. Kidd, 1922
Cat. No. QFA 233

Pipe.

Nigeria, Kwale Ibo, 19th Century

The style of this double-bowled terra cotta pipe is very rare. There are approximately fifteen known complete examples, all reported to have been collected in the late 19th Century and to be located in Great Britain. In addition, three fragments were found at Osisa, Nigeria, in 1955. However, it is believed that this particular piece is the only pipe in this style which is made of pottery. The known pieces were placed on the altar consecrated to the cult of the Yam Spirit, and there is no reason to doubt that this pipe was also associated with that function. The pipe was collected by the donor's brother, Captain Harold Dyer, at Afikpo in Southern Nigeria in 1902. Length: 17.8 cm.

Donor:
Mrs. Dyer Thompson, 1935
Cat. No. F 27

Leg Band.

Congo, date unknown

This leg band is made from a solid brass rod which is rounded at the ends and flattened throughout the middle portion. Incised and sculptured geometric designs cover the outside surface of the flat area. While leg bands were in general use in much of Central Africa, it is difficult to imagine an individual wearing one of the size and weight of this piece. This is one of a small number of artifacts given to the Museum which were collected by the donor's grandfather during his missionary years in Africa. Height: 15.2 cm. Diameter: 12.7 cm.

Donor:
P.W. Holman, 1950
Cat. No. F 766

Comb.

Kenya, Possibly Masai, date unknown

Carved from a single piece of wood, this unpainted comb features the sculptured figure of a bird at one end and incised geometric designs on both sides. The comb was collected by the missionary parents of the donor and, along with a large quantity of material from East and Central Africa, was eventually given to the Museum. The Museum's collection of ethnological artifacts from Africa numbers some 1300 items; ten, including the comb, are illustrated in this catalogue. Height: 36.8 cm.

Donor:
Mrs. R. Morrow, 1947
Cat. No. F 755

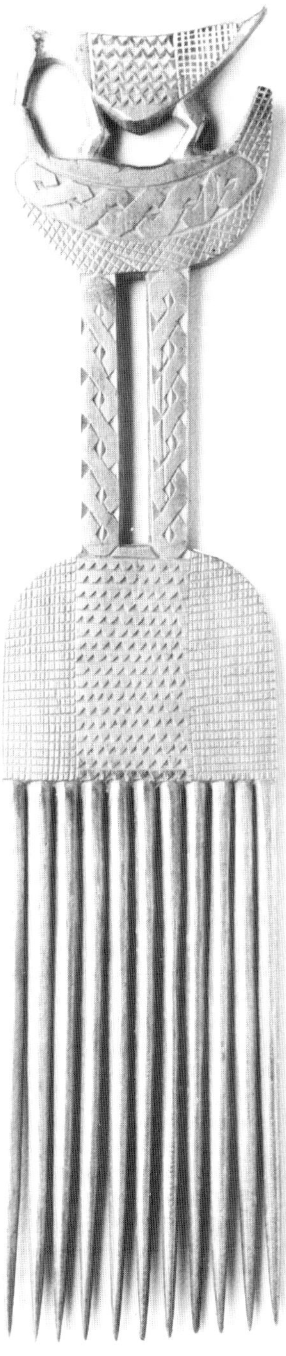

Masks, *Mba.*

Afikpo, Nigeria, Ibo, 19th Century

Both of these masks are called *Mba,* a term which refers to the type of wood from which they are carved and the type of costume worn with them. They have a woven plant fibre frame attached to the back which serves to cover the face. While they now appear only partially covered in black and red-brown pigments, they were probably originally coloured in traditional form in black, white, red-orange and yellow. *Mba* masks are used in various masquerades of the men's village secret society, especially in a satiric play, *ɔkumkpa.* This is the most popular and well attended Afikpo masked ritual and consists of a series of skits, songs, and dances. The mask on the left, with the cutout sections in the top, is of a form called *mkpere* and is used exclusively in a particular ceremony. It is believed that these examples are the earliest known dated masks from Afikpo. They were collected from there in 1902 by the donor's brother, Captain Harold Dyer, who had become the first District Officer of the area as a result of Lord Baden-Powell's recommendation and a successful campaign. Height: 43.2-48.3 cm.

Donor:
Mrs. Dyer Thomson, 1935
Cat. Nos. (left) F 72, (right) F 48

Stool.

Possibly West Africa, date unknown

Carved in the form of a full figure elephant on which a seat is mounted, this stool is made from a single piece of wood. It is unpainted but has, at some time in the past, been varnished. Although there are features of this piece that suggest a similarity to West African chieftain stools, the appearance of the elephant figure is somewhat unusual, thereby placing its provenance in doubt. Height: 57.2 cm.

Donor:
Reverend Cecil Cherry, 1946
Cat. No. F 59

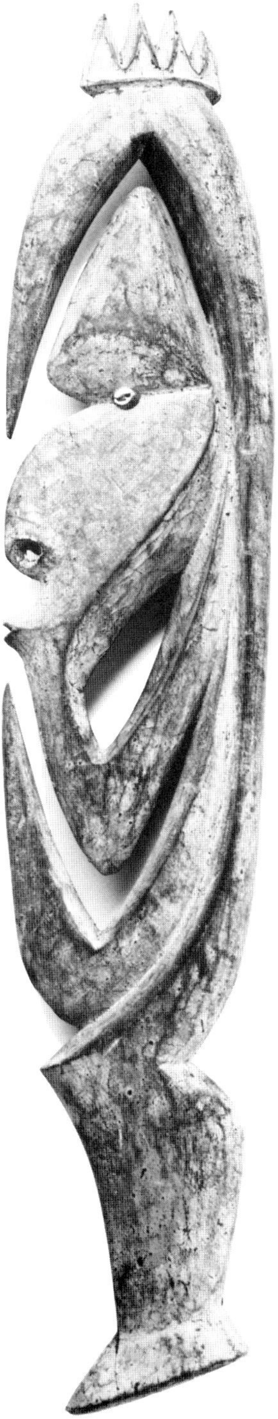

Sculpture.
New Guinea, Sepik, date unknown

This sculptured stylized human figure with cowrie shell eyes is carved from wood. On the surface, there are traces of what would appear to be ochre and a black stain. This piece has been identified as a basket hook, a device used for suspending food baskets or nets from the ceiling. It bears a close resemblance to the *kamanggabi* figures, and to various large sculptured cult or spirit figures which are owned by clans and kept in the men's ceremonial houses, where, as oracles, they are consulted before campaigns and hunting expeditions. Height: 63.5 cm.

Donor:
W. Philip Mathews, 1978
Cat. No. ED 293

Mask.
Fly River, New Guinea, date unknown

Carved from a single piece of wood, this mask is coloured with red ochre, charcoal and lime, and edged with small shells which also decorate the eyebrows. The eyes are inlaid cowrie shells. Reportedly made prior to 1914 and used on ceremonial occasions, the mask is similar to those which represent ancestral spirits and are made and kept in the men's house. Height: 85.1 cm.

Donor:
John C. Castle-Burns, 1965
Cat. No. ED 89

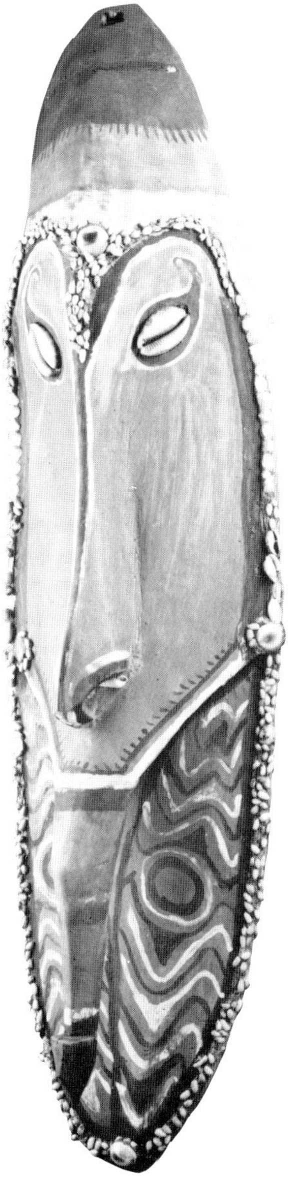

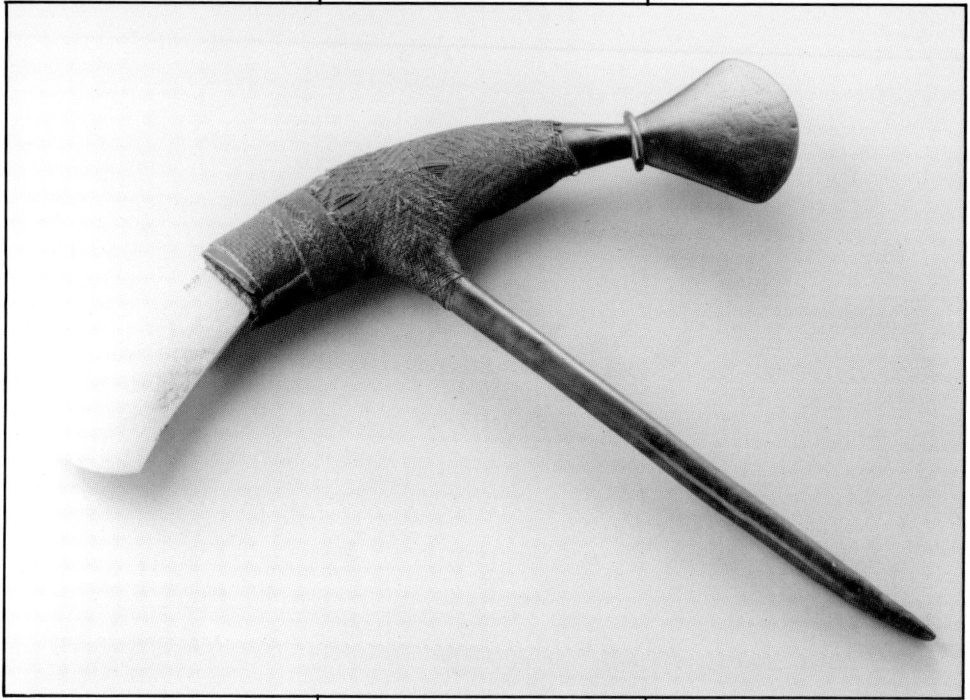

Axe.
Mt. Hagen, New Guinea, date unknown

This axe consists of a pale grey-green coloured stone blade fitted into a wooden haft which is partially bound with woven split cane, now blackish in colour. Axes of this type are peculiar to the Mt. Hagen area of the New Guinea highlands and are used ceremonially, for trade and in battle. Prior to the arrival of the white man, the two major items of native trade were the ceremonial axe and salt. Although it is still traded and prized, its value has fallen as a consequence of the introduction of the steel axe. The axe has been valued approximately on a par with a gold-lip shell, the premier object of personal wealth. Length: 50.8 cm, Width: 55.9 cm.

Donor:
Eric W. Were, 1958
Cat. No. ED 39

Ornament, **kap-kap.**
Yule Island, New Guinea,
date unknown

This ornament, known as *kap-kap,* is made from a disc of turtleshell cut into an open-work pattern and superimposed on a disc of tridacna shell. Traditionally worn on the breast or forehead and with the turtle-shell elements showing many variants in detail, ornaments of this type have a wide distribution throughout Melanesia. Although worn mainly by men, these ornaments have also appeared on the back of women's dance costumes. Maximum diameter: 11.4cm.

Donor:
John C. Castle-Burns, 1965
Cat. No. ED 96

Club
Santa Cruz Islands,
date unknown

Carved from wood, this dance club is encircled with a fringe of bast and partially painted in red and black with fine rectilinear designs which, without exception, derive from fish and bird motifs. Two small bird heads appear in relief on the top surface. Traditionally, clubs of this type were given the shape of bird figures. Now, this motif is scarcely recognizable and, in fact, it has been remarked that the form of the club resembles that of the canoes from the area. While the significance of the club is obscure, it is known to have been used for ceremonial dances. Length: 86.4 cm.

Donor:
Dr. E. Newton-Drier, 1934
Cat. No. ED 207

Comb.
Solomon Islands, date unknown

This comb has a triangular body of thirteen gummed and bound wooden prongs of palm wood. It has been blackened and inlaid with segments of pearl shell. A wooden stem extends from the top of the body, which is bound with twisted fibre cord and covered with gum. Combs such as this one originate from the south-eastern region of the Solomons and were worn in the hair, mainly by the men. This particular piece was collected by the donor in New Zealand in 1912. The Museum's collection of ethnological artifacts from Oceania number some 670 items; nine, including the comb, are illustrated in this catalogue. Length: 27.9 cm.

Donor:
W.A. Wellband, 1975
Cat. No. ED 222

Canoe Prow Ornament, *nguzu nguzu.*
Solomon Islands, date unknown

Carved of wood in the form of a stylized human head with slight prognathous, this ornament has been blackened and inlaid with pearl shell, which comprises the eyes and the facial ornamentation. Large natural coloured wood pierced ears have been added. While ornaments such as this one vary in shape and attitude, they still retain their characteristic features of the projecting jaw and concave nose. Fastened just above the waterline on the prows of war canoes, *tomako,* these ornaments represented guardian spirits who protected the canoes from accidents at sea and exercised a malign influence on the enemy under attack. The war canoes were noted for their great size and elaborate decoration. Some measured over 18.3 metres in length with prow and stern posts up to 4.6 metres in height. Others, with low bows, had extra washstrakes to prevent the entry of water. With a 1.8 metre beam amidships, these canoes could carry nearly one hundred men. Decoration was primarily in the form of shell inlay and attachments. Shells, decorated bamboo tubes containing magical substances, and streamers were attached to the prow and stern, and small figure carvings, including the canoe prow ornament, were attached at various points. Unusual in Melanesia, Solomon Islands canoes were plank-built and the seams caulked with crushed parinarium seed (putty-nut). This method of construction allowed a wider beam, gave greater stability and made an outrigger unnecessary. Height: 17.8 cm.

Donor:
Mrs. C. Gardner Johnson, 1928
Cat. No. ED 204

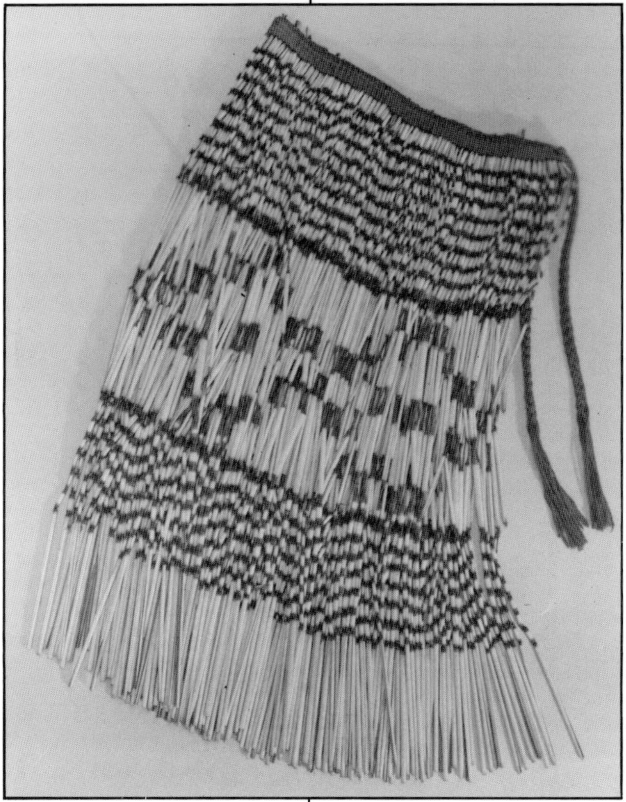

Kilt, *piupiu*.
New Zealand — Maori, date unknown

This kilt is made of woven flax. Each strip has been scraped at intervals and the ends plaited into a narrow waist band. Left in the sun, the unscraped parts curl into tubes. When the kilt is dyed, only the scraped portions darken. The flax in these dark areas has been twisted. Kilts have always been popular and were occasionally worn about the shoulders. Although this form of garment dates back to the time of Captain James Cook's first visit to the islands in 1769-1770, they are now the usual dress of the modern Maori in traditional displays. Length: 72.4 cm. Width: 73.7 cm.

Donor: Mr. P. Nichols, 1978
Cat. No. EB 50

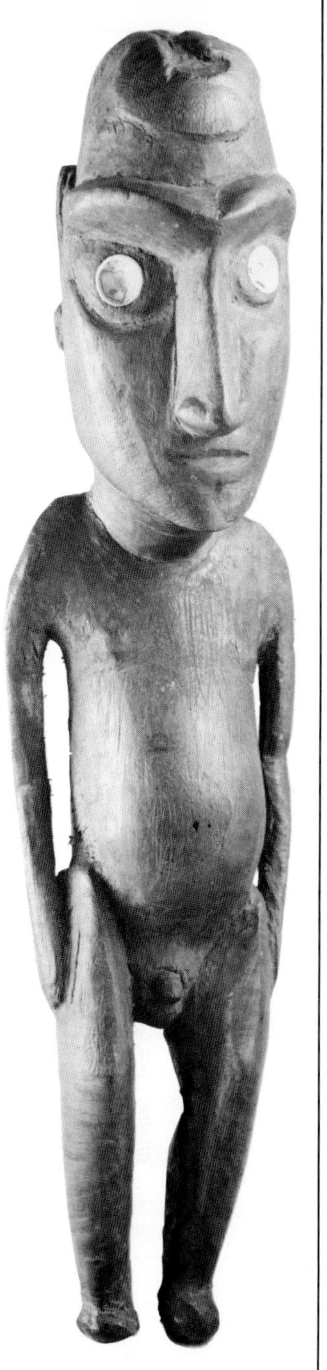

Effigy.
Easter Island, 19th Century

This effigy is carved in the form of a standing male figure, from a single piece of wood. The eyes are of inlaid shell. Little is known of the wooden figures from this island. It would appear, however, that the smaller images were a development of the latter half of the 19th century, a period of artistic degeneration, when thick, massive and usually roughly finished figures were carved for commercial purposes. Small figures, such as this one normally represented ancestors and had a ritual significance. In addition, they probably served as ornaments. With a great scarcity of trees on the island, a species of mimosa called "toromiro" being the only one of any size, wood was a rare and costly material. Height: 36.8 cm.

Donor: Lieutenant G.T. Emmons, 1924
Cat. No. EC 2

DEPARTMENTAL HISTORIES

History

In 1968 the History Department of the Vancouver Museum was established to collect, preserve, and exhibit artifacts which reflected the development of Vancouver from the mid-nineteenth century to the present. In additon, the department gathered material which, although without specific local relationship, illustrated the cultural heritage of the early immigrant populations, especially those of the British Isles. These collections were based on material donated to the museum itself but more importantly, were also based on the artifacts and memorabilia collected by the founder of the Vancouver City Archives, Major James Skitt Matthews.

Major Matthews (1878-1970) began his collection of Vancouver mementos in 1929, when few recognized the importance of preserving the city's history. He salvaged wonderful curiosities and souvenirs from the citizens' past, and took great joy in searching for artifacts related to obscure firsts and lasts, such as the first European child born in Vancouver, the mailbox from the first farm, the leg shackles worn by the last chain gang, and so on.

In 1980 with the creation of the Decorative Arts Department, the History collections were edited to concentrate more closely on objects related to the history of the city. The artifacts of general European interest were transferred to the new department, and the History Department retained local material and the large costume collection and toy collections.

Since 1968 the department has had four curators, beginning with Mr. James Stanton, followed by Mrs. Kerry McPhedran in 1971, Mr. Robb Watt in 1973 , and Mr. Ivan Sayers in 1979. In addition there have been numerous curatorial assistants and volunteers who have worked on programmes to organize and document the collections, conduct research projects, and assist with the preparation of displays. From the outset the department has had an active interpretation programme involving permanent and temporary exhibitions. There are three major and semi-permanent galleries entitled "Exploration and Settlement","Milltown", and "Vancouver, the Metropolis". The first describes historic events on the coast of British Columbia (c. 1700-1860). The second deals with the first commercial forestry enterprises and the resulting village communities (c. 1860-1889), and the third gallery illustrates some of the domestic lifestyles and architecture of the city from the turn of the century until the beginning of the First World War. The next and final phase of this series will be the gallery, "Vancouver at War" which will discuss how the people of the city dealt with the problems created by both World Wars and the Great Depression of the 1930's. Since 1968, the topics covered by temporary exhibitions have been very wide-ranging. Exhibitions have included "Impressions of An Age", featuring 19th century B.C. artists and their portrayals of the new settlements (1969); Pioneer Life gallery (1968-1972); "Ho For the Klondike" (1970'1971); "Vancouver Between the Streets". Vancouver's architectural heritage (1974); "Sounds, Samplers and Toys", early gramaphones and selections from the sampler and toy collections (1975-1976); "Rainbows in Our Walls: Art and Stained Glass in Vancouver 1890-1940 (1978-1979), "The World of Children" (1979-1980), Les Chapeaux; the Fashionable Woman's Hat 1750-1950 (1979-1980); "Waisted Efforts: Women's Undergarments 1760-1960" (1981-1982).

Natural History

The first constitution (1894)of the Art, Historical and Scientific Association of Vancouver, appeared to give pride of place to ethnological studies and collecting. Yet it is significant that the first recorded donation to the collections of the Association's museum was a natural history specimen, a swan. Of the first lectures sponsored by the Association, one was on art, one on archaeology and the third on "The Geology of Burrard Inlet", given by G.F. Monckton, M.E. While the support given to natural history collecting and interpretation has varied over the years, its place in the life of the Museum has often been much greater than a glance at paid staff and formal structures might indicate. To date, the most active periods have been the 1920s and 1930s and the late 1960s and early 1970s.

In 1924, T.P.O Menzies, an entomologist, was appointed as the Museum's secretary-curator. Two years later, on 13 February 1926, the Burrard Field Naturalist Society was formed at a meeting held at the Museum. Over the next two decades this active group of academics and keen amateurs took an active part in rearranging and reorganizing the natural history collections of the Museum. The club was organized into a number of sections; Geology, Botany, Ornithology, Entomology, Marine Biology and Zoology. Some of the heads of these sections were Directors of the Assocation and many were contributors to the Museum's quarterly "Museum and Art Notes". They were so active in this latter forum that readers not residing in Vancouver might easily have felt that the institution was essentially a natural history museum. During this same period, the Museum received its greatest and most significant natural history bequest, the Newton Drier Collection of molluscs, totalling some 3/4 million specimens. The donor, Dr. E. Newton Drier, acted as Honorary Curator of Conchology, as funds did not permit establishing a staff position. By the mid 1960's, as the Museum prepared to move to a new site, the curator characterized the strengths of the natural history collection as conchology, entomology and British Columbia ornithology.

The natural history department was established in 1968 and for a brief period was staffed by a number of professionals who hoped to establish zoological and botanical collections and related field programmes which would support the

Natural History Display in Carnegie Library building.

development of a museum to study the natural history of the Pacific Rim. Chief Curator Dr. Robert H. Carcasson (1968-1972) was a noted entomologist; Curator Earl Olson (1968-1971) was a herpetologist, and Associate Curator Geoff Stewart (1968-1975) was also a zoologist. Preparations for elaborate new natural history displays meant that these men undertook from 1969-1971 the first natural history field investigations funded by the Museum. One of these galleries was completed, made possible also by the presence of a staff taxidermist, Hans Meyer (1969-1974). This was entitled"Sounds of Life," which opened in October 1971 and closed in September 1974. Regrettably neither the City nor the Association were able to support the costs of collecting and interpreting natural history in contemporary fashion. Three natural historians, Tabe Flett (1975), Brian Barrett (1975) and Robin Weber (1975-1981) administered the Department while the role of natural history in the institution was re-assessed. The role has now been defined with a strong regional emphasis. The current departmental objective is:

> "to develop collections related to the botany, geology, geography and zoology of the Lower Mainland of British Columbia with particular emphasis on the Greater Vancouver Regional District".

The aim is to re-establish the department with a curator who will provide access to the existing collections of molluscs and mineral, zoological and paleontological specimens and establish new resources through field collecting.

Archaeology

Although he was never officially known as such, Charles Hill-Tout might properly be called the Musuem's first Curator of Archaeology. His long involvement with the Art Scientific and Historical Association as founding member and president from 1894 to 1944 and his fascination with the cultures and pre-history of B.C.'s native peoples ensured that archaeological collections and studies received considerable attention. Hill-Tout's intellect and imagination were most aroused by what came to be called the Great Fraser Midden, a huge site located on the north shore of the Fraser in the Vancouver suburb of Marpole. Hill-Tout first became aware of it in 1902 when roadwork extensively disturbed the site. He was able, with fellow AHSA member G.F. Monckton to survey the 4.5 acre site. Regrettably, lack of funds delayed further site study for 28 years until 1930 when Herman Leask undertook excavations sponsored by the Museum. Members of the Association rightly considered this field-work and the resulting collections as one of the two most important accomplishments of the AHSA's first fifty years.

Given Hill-Tout's enthusiasm for B.C. prehistory, it is not surprising that the Museum's archaeological efforts were concentrated in this area. After World War II, the Museum continued its support of the field, despite the limited extent of its resources, by employing as Curator of Anthropology and Paleontology, Elma von Engel-Baiersdorf. With Mrs. Baiersdorf's arrival at the Museum, some smaller sections of the archaeological collections which included an 1800-year old Egyptian mummy, received expert study and interpretation. Her findings were published in the second series of the Museum and Art Notes. The same publication also included reports and research notes by Carl Borden, Lecturer in archaeology at U.B.C. and widely regarded now as the father of modern archaeology in British Columbia. Ultimately, Mr. Borden became active as a Trustee of the Museum and it was undoubtedly his own work and interests which ensured that an archaelogist was included in the expanded body of professionals who began working with the Museum in 1968 following the move to Vanier Park.

The department was founded in 1968 and the first Curator of Archaeology was Gay Calvert (1968-1970). Her brief tenure included a very active period of field excavation - the important Fraser Delta site of St. Mungo Cannery (reported in B.C. Studies, Nos. 6-7, pp. 54-75) - and development of a permanent gallery. This display opened in 1970 and incorporated the results of much of the new fieldwork undertaken by Borden and others in the region since 1950. Calvert was succeeded by Bjorn Simonsen (1970- 1972) and then the Curator of Ethnology, Lynn Maranda, in an acting capacity. Sumie Imamoto, curatorial assistant in 1977, was curator from 1979 - 1981.

Since the Calvert excavations, no fieldwork has been undertaken. However, present plans foresee a major new interpretive gallery and a new programme of fieldwork prior to 1986.

Decorative and Applied Arts

The department of Decorative and Applied Arts was created in 1979 in response to a collections policy document prepared in 1977 which stated that: "The Centennial Museum should collect, preserve and interpret the human and natural history of the Lower Mainland region with special emphasis given to the development of collections and exhibitions of decorative and applied arts from the three cultures forming the principal heritage of this region, Canada, Europe and Asia". Carol E. Mayer was appointed first curator in January 1979. Although the department of Decorative and Applied Arts is relatively new the collections, originally housed in either Ethnology or History, date back to the early days of the museum. Perhaps one of the first significant donations that laid the foundation for the eventual formation of this new department was a collection of bronzes from Thailand. They were loaned in 1907 by Dr. W.A. Briggs who had spent twenty-eight years as a medical missionary in Thailand. During that time he developed a keen interest in 'curios' and built a fine collection of over two hundred and fifty pieces.

The total collection was donated by Mrs. Briggs and the family in 1927. In 1941 a significant collection of Japanese tsuba was donated by the daughter of Captain James Inman, a British diplomat who had retired to England after living in Vancouver for many years. These tsuba combined with those acquired from Captain Henry Pybus in 1900, form the core of the Japanese collection and have been the focus of much scholarly attention. In 1946 Vancouver celebrated its Golden Jubilee and Mrs. Edith Clark chose this occasion to donate her collection of Chinese material. Mrs. Clark had worked as a missionary in China and upon her return to Vancouver she became a stalwart supporter of the museum which was then housed on the top floor of the Carnegie library at Hastings and Main. She hoped that by donating her own collection to the museum, the city would recognize the need for new premises. In recognition of her efforts on behalf of the museum Mrs. Clark was appointed Honorary Curator of Oriental Art in 1946. This same honour was bestowed upon Mr. Frederick O'Grady in 1950 for his donation of Chinese porcelain and bronzes. In 1949 Mrs. Mary Lipsett donated her collection of Asian material which included ceramics, textiles, bronzes, jades, ivories and snuff bottles. By 1960 the Asian collection had grown to over two thousand pieces and was recognized as an important and prominent element of the museum's holdings. The collection continues to grow and the Vancouver Museum plans to

Snuff bottle. Cat. No: DA 570.

open two permanent galleries of Asian Decorative and Applied Arts in 1984.

The European section of the collection did not receive a substantial donation until 1966 when Mr. R. Wilson Galbraith donated his fine collection of porcelain and glass. Unlike the Asian donations which tended to come in large numbers the European donations came in ones and twos and consequently the growth of the collection was slow. There is no doubt that Mr. Galbraith's donation provided the much needed basis for the development of a European decorative arts collection. The emphasis is still very much focused on porcelain, glass and silver but textiles and furniture will be gaining more prominence in the next few years in preparation for the installation of a permanent European Decorative and Applied Arts gallery. The Canadian collection, although small at this time, is indicative of the new direction that the museum is taking. The need to collect 'Canadiana' has been recognized and to date we have acquired some fine examples of Canadian silver and glass. As with the other two sections of the Decorative and Applied Arts department we are planning to open a permanent 'Canadiana' gallery within the next few years. Prior to 1979 there were a number of exhibitions held at the Vancouver Museum which foreshadowed the interpretation programme of the new department. These included Soochow Embroidery - contemporary Chinese arts and crafts (1974), Within the Potters House - world-wide collection of ceramics (1976) and Treasures of London - masterpieces from the collection of The Worshipful Company of Goldsmiths (1977).

Since 1979 the new department has been responsible for eight exhibitions which have continued to demonstrate the range of decorative and applied arts at the Vancouver Museum. These include Patterns of Persia - Nomadic and City rugs from Iran (1979), Kogo - Japanese incense boxes (1980), Tea and Coffee - 18th - 20th century British procelain (1981), The Look of Music - the artistic and historical development of European musical instruments 1500-1900 (1980) and The Comfortable Arts - weaving traditions of Canada (1982). It is hoped that the Decorative and Applied Arts department will continue to maintain a high profile at the Vancouver Museum both in the areas of exhibitions and research. Looking towards the future the new department recognizes that the arts are an integral part of all people's heritage and should be preserved for the enjoyment and education of future generations.

Ethnology

Ethnology had its beginnings in this museum in 1968. Although the formation of this scientific discipline was relatively recent, the museum had been building ethnological collections since 1895. The first recorded acquisition was the purchase of "Indian Curios".

Between 1895 and 1968, the museum's ethnological activities were highlighted with major acquisitions. These included: Dr. W.A. Briggs collection from Siam (1907); Pauline Johnson bequest (1913); Nootka canoe brought by members of the Art, Historical and Scientific Association from Harrison Mills to Stanley Park by sail and oar (1924); Mrs. C. Gardner Johnson collection from Oceania (1928); Captain Harold Dyer collection from Southern Nigeria (1935); Oriental collections from Mrs. E. Clark (1946), Edward and Mary Lipsett (1949), and Mrs. Jonathan Rogers (1960). Within this period, noteworthy ethnological projects included: a proposed Indian Village for Stanley Park (1915-1925); the first cataloguing programme (1961-1963); insurance evaluation programme (1964-1967); Material Culture Holdings Locator (1967).

In 1968, City Museum collections were moved to new quarters at the Centennial Museum, and separate disciplinary functions for Natural History, Archaeology, Ethnology and History were established. Having its own defined collection, a professional footing was established and the new Department of Ethnology under its first Curator, Lynn Maranda launched a variety of scientific and creative programmes. The collections were examined, organized, and the process of cataloguing established again. Since 1968, the collections have been documented and redocumented, assessed and reassessed many times. Between 1982 and 1977, much of the work on the collections was funded by Local Initiatives Programme grants and the Ethnology Department took advantage of this wealth of labour to research, catalogue and photograph its holdings. L.I.P. workers compiled bibliographies, established an archival photograph file, conducted field investigations, undertook research projects, assembled locator files for all collections, and prepared the B.C. Native Artisan File.

The ethnology collections have continued to grow and since 1968, major acquisitions have included: Edward and Mary Lipsett collection (1971); Dr. and Mrs. C.A. Ryan collection of Haida argillite carvings (1974); repatriated Pacific Northwest Coast pieces funded by the Government of Canada under the Cultural Property Export and Import Act (1981, 1982).

With the growth of material culture in the museum, the ethnological collections attracted interest from all parts of the world. Selected items have been researched for numerous scholarly interests and publications, and others have been sought nationally and internationally for important exhibitions, appearing in: Chicago, (1964, 1982); Paris, France (1969); Ottawa (1969, 1981); Phoenix (1979); Hamburg, West Germany (1979).

Continuing with the history of the use of the collections, it is noted that since 1968, the Ethnology Department has been responsible for numerous major exhibitions,including: "Age of Edenshaw" (1968), which coincided with the opening of the new museum; "Material Culture of the Pacific Northwest Coast Indians" which ran as an exhibition of the permanent collections from 1971 to 1980; "The River People", a travelling exhibition which toured throughout B.C. between 1976 and 1979; the museum's premier international exhibition, "Discovery 1778: Captain James Cook and the Peoples of the Pacific" (1978) co-ordinated for the bicentennial of Cook's Third Voyage to the Pacific; "George Forster 1754-1794: A German Pacific Expert of the 18th Century, Enlightenment Philosopher and Anthropologist Revolutionary" (1978), an important exhibition from Germany.

In 1979, a new department of Decorative and Applied Arts was established and some 2,000 pieces of the Asian collection were transferred from Ethnology to the new discipline. The present ethnological collection numbers some 9,000 pieces from the Pacific Northwest, North America, Central and South America, Asia, Africa and Oceania.

It has been the function of Ethnology to acquire, preserve and manage collections for the uses they serve in research, education and exhibition, and to promote a greater understanding of the material culture of man.

I N D E X

I N D E X